Low Pressure Boilers *fourth edition*

Study Guide

atp AMERICAN TECHNICAL PUBLISHERS
ORLAND PARK, ILLINOIS 60467-5756

Frederick M. Steingress

Low Pressure Boilers Study Guide contains procedures commonly practiced in industry and the trade. Specific procedures vary with each task and must be performed by a qualified person. For maximum safety, always refer to specific manufacturer recommendations, insurance regulations, specific job site and plant procedures, applicable federal, state, and local regulations, and any authority having jurisdiction. The material contained is intended to be an educational resource for the user. American Technical Publishers, Inc. assumes no responsibility or liability in connection with this material or its use by any individual or organization.

Technical information and assistance was also provided by the following companies, organizations, and individuals:

ITT Bell & Gossett
Cleaver-Brooks
Honeywell Inc.

Quick Quiz, Quick Quizzes, and Master Math are either registered trademarks or trademarks of American Technical Publishers, Inc.

4 5 6 7 8 9 – 13 – 9 8 7 6 5 4 3 2

Printed in the United States of America

ISBN 978-0-8269-4366-8

 This book is printed on recycled paper.

Contents

Low Pressure Boilers Study Guide is designed to reinforce information presented in *Low Pressure Boilers*. The textbook is used as a reference to complete the learning activities in the study guide. Each chapter in the study guide covers information in the corresponding chapter in the textbook. Chapter 12 – Boiler Operator Licensing contains seven separate exams that can be used as a comprehensive review. The questions in Chapter 12 are similar to the type of questions found on a typical boiler operator licensing examination.

Answering Chapter Questions

The question types used in the study guide include true-false, multiple choice, matching, and essay. For true-false questions, circle the letter T if the statement is true, or circle the letter F if the statement is false. For multiple choice questions, place the letter of the correct answer in the answer blank next to the question. For matching questions, place the letter of the correct corresponding answer in the answer blank next to the question. For essay questions, write the answers on a separate sheet of paper and submit to the instructor.

ASME Code Symbol Stamps

At the bottom of the first page in Chapters 1 through 11, a new ASME Code symbol stamp and its meaning is introduced. This allows progressive learning of the symbol stamps used on various boiler room equipment. Chapter 12 checks for understanding of the symbol stamps presented throughout the study guide.

Related Information

Information presented in *Low Pressure Boilers* and the *Low Pressure Boilers Study Guide* addresses common boiler operation topics. Additional information related to boiler operation/stationary engineering is available in other American Technical Publishers products. To obtain information about these products, visit the American Technical Publishers website at www.go2atp.com.

The Publisher

Name _____ Date _____

True-False

T	F	**1.**	Steam is formed when water is heated to its boiling point.
T	F	**2.**	A boiler is an open metal container in which water is heated to produce steam or heated water.
T	F	**3.**	Water begins to boil at 212°F at atmospheric pressure.
T	F	**4.**	In a Scotch marine boiler, the gases of combustion pass through tubes that are surrounded by water.
T	F	**5.**	Oxygen is needed to burn fuel.
T	F	**6.**	Condensate is typically returned to the boiler for reuse.
T	F	**7.**	The steam system supplies water to the boiler.
T	F	**8.**	Steam leaves the boiler through the main steam line.
T	F	**9.**	Steam that has given up its heat and turned back to water is boiler water.
T	F	**10.**	Heat is generated in a boiler by the combustion of a fuel such as gas, fuel oil, or coal.
T	F	**11.**	An internal furnace is a furnace in a boiler that is surrounded by heating surface.
T	F	**12.**	Feedwater is water that is treated for use in a boiler.
T	F	**13.**	Heat always flows from a material having a lower temperature to a material having a higher temperature.
T	F	**14.**	Latent heat is heat identified by a change of state and no temperature change of the substance.
T	F	**15.**	Conduction is heat transfer that occurs when molecules in a material are heated and the heat is passed from molecule to molecule through the material.
T	F	**16.**	Approximately 212 lb of air are required to burn a pound of fuel.
T	F	**17.**	The ASME Code governs boiler design, material, method of construction, inspection, and quality assurance.

ASME CODE SYMBOL STAMP	Before 2013	2013 and After	HEATING BOILER
	H	ASME / H	

T   F   **18.** A low pressure boiler is a boiler that has an MAWP over 15 psi.

T   F   **19.** A package boiler is a self-contained unit that is preassembled at the factory.

T   F   **20.** A firebox boiler is a cylindrical scotch marine boiler.

Multiple Choice

_____ **1.** ___ is necessary to generate steam in a boiler.
    A. A container
    B. Water
    C. Heat
    D. all of the above

_____ **2.** The ___ is the part of the boiler with water on one side and heat on the other.
    A. furnace volume
    B. heating surface
    C. fire side
    D. water side

_____ **3.** A ___ boiler has heat and gases of combustion that pass through tubes surrounded by water.
    A. firetube
    B. watertube
    C. cast iron
    D. straight-tube

_____ **4.** A ___ boiler has water in the tubes and heat and gases of combustion passing around the tubes.
    A. firetube
    B. watertube
    C. cast iron
    D. firebox

_____ **5.** ___ are used in boilers to direct the gases of combustion over the boiler heating surface.
    A. Combustion controls
    B. Firetubes
    C. Baffles
    D. Zone controls

_____ **6.** Sensible heat is heat that ___.
    A. involves a change of state
    B. has no temperature change of the substance
    C. changes ice to water
    D. can be measured with a thermometer

_____ **7.** A ___ is used to transfer heat from one substance to another without allowing the materials to mix.

    A. thermometer

    B. heat exchanger

    C. thermostat

    D. regulator

_____ **8.** In the ___, air mixes with fuel and burns.

    A. tube sheet

    B. watertubes

    C. combustion chamber

    D. breeching

_____ **9.** ___ combustion is combustion that occurs when fuel is burned using only the theoretical amount of air.

    A. Perfect

    B. Incomplete

    C. Complete

    D. Partial efficient

_____ **10.** ___ air is air supplied to a burner above the theoretical amount required to burn the fuel to ensure complete combustion.

    A. Primary

    B. Excess

    C. Secondary

    D. Pilot

_____ **11.** The breaking up of fuel into small particles to maximize contact of fuel with air for combustion is ___.

    A. steam priming

    B. convection loading

    C. atomization

    D. discharge shaping

_____ **12.** The ___ system provides the air necessary for combustion.

    A. feedwater

    B. draft

    C. steam

    D. fuel

_____ **13.** The ___ is the highest pressure in pounds per square inch at which a boiler can safely be operated.

    A. NOWL

    B. ASME

    C. MAWP

    D. LWFC

_____ **14.** A ___ boiler does not use tubes.
    A. cast iron
    B. scotch marine
    C. watertube
    D. firebox

_____ **15.** To increase efficiency of the boiler, ___.
    A. more fuel is added
    B. firetubes are decreased in size
    C. the heating surface is increased
    D. all of the above

_____ **16.** The four systems necessary to operate a boiler are ___, ___, ___, and ___.
    A. combustion; draft; steam; boiler water
    B. water; steam; combustion; stoker
    C. boiler water; fuel; draft; condensate
    D. feedwater; fuel; draft; steam

_____ **17.** ___ pressure is the pressure caused by the weight of air surrounding the earth.
    A. Atmospheric
    B. Thermal
    C. Conductive
    D. Absolute

_____ **18.** During operation, a boiler ___.
    A. holds water
    B. collects the steam that is produced
    C. transfers heat to the water to produce steam
    D. all of the above

_____ **19.** Water turns to steam at ___°F at atmospheric pressure.
    A. 100
    B. 150
    C. 200
    D. 212

_____ **20.** ___ boilers have sections that can be assembled on-site to produce the boiler capacity required.
    A. Firetube
    B. Industrial watertube
    C. Scotch marine
    D. Cast iron

_____ **21.** The amount of energy required to raise the temperature of 1 lb of water 1°F is 1 ___.
    A. NOWL
    B. therm
    C. psia
    D. Btu

_____ **22.** Heat is transferred by ___.
  A. conduction
  B. convection
  C. radiation
  D. all of the above

_____ **23.** A(n) ___ is a component directly attached to the boiler that is required for the operation of the boiler.
  A. fitting
  B. accessory
  C. fuel oil tank
  D. condensate return tank

_____ **24.** The nonflammable material used to insulate the outer surface of the boiler from heat is ___.
  A. refractory
  B. steam bridge
  C. aquastat
  D. tube bank

_____ **25.** ___ is pure steam at a temperature that corresponds to the boiling point of water at a specific pressure.
  A. Clean steam
  B. Condensate
  C. Enthalpy
  D. Saturated steam

Boiler Systems

_____ **1.** Steam system

_____ **2.** Boiler

_____ **3.** Feedwater system

_____ **4.** Draft system

_____ **5.** Fuel system

Scotch Marine Boiler

_____ 1. Tubes

_____ 2. Tube sheet

_____ 3. Gases of combustion

_____ 4. Internal furnace

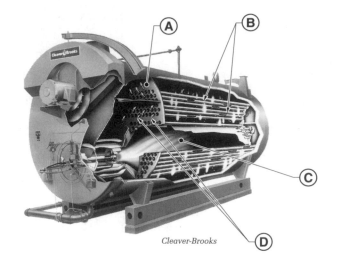

Cleaver-Brooks

Steam Heating System

_____ 1. Condensate receiver tank

_____ 2. Main steam line

_____ 3. Feedwater pump

_____ 4. Steam header

_____ 5. Branch lines

_____ 6. Main steam stop valve

_____ 7. Heating unit

_____ 8. Steam trap

_____ 9. Boiler

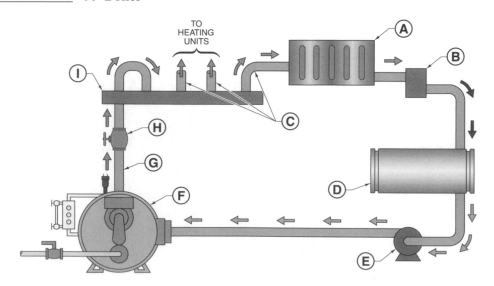

HRT Boiler

_____ **1.** Furnace

_____ **2.** Gases of combustion

_____ **3.** Sling

_____ **4.** Tube sheet

_____ **5.** Bridge wall

_____ **6.** Boiler

_____ **7.** Steel beam

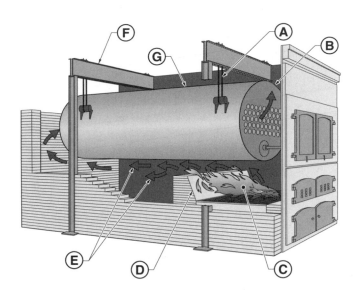

Straight-Tube Watertube Boiler

_____ **1.** Steam and water drum

_____ **2.** Internal feedwater line

_____ **3.** Tubes

_____ **4.** Gases of combustion

_____ **5.** Furnace

_____ **6.** Burner assembly

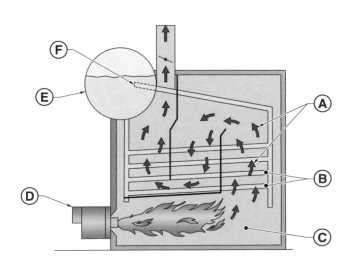

Additional Activities

1. Review Chapter 1 of *Low Pressure Boilers.*

2. Take the Quick Quiz® for Chapter 1 on the *Low Pressure Boilers* Interactive CD-ROM.

3. Review the following related Media Clips on the *Low Pressure Boilers* Interactive CD-ROM:
   - Combustion Efficiency
   - Electric Boilers
   - Firetube Boilers
   - Heating Surface
   - Low Pressure Boilers
   - MAWP
   - Package Boilers
   - Watertube Boilers

4. Review the Flash Cards for Chapter 1 on the *Low Pressure Boilers* Interactive CD-ROM.

5. Optionally, review the Master Math® Applications, Unit 1 to Unit 4, located on the *Low Pressure Boilers* Interactive CD-ROM. A link to a PDF document, Boiler Math Formulas, is provided on the Master Math® Applications home page.

Name _____ Date _____

True-False

T	F	**1.**	Boiler fittings are components attached directly to the boiler.
T	F	**2.**	Safety valves on steam boilers are designed to open slowly.
T	F	**3.**	The safety valve should chatter to prevent damage to the disc.
T	F	**4.**	Safety valves are tested only by performing a try lever test.
T	F	**5.**	A safety valve try lever test is performed with the boiler at 15 psi or higher.
T	F	**6.**	The steam pressure gauge must be connected to the highest part of the steam side of the boiler.
T	F	**7.**	A siphon is connected between the boiler and the steam pressure gauge to prevent water from entering the Bourdon tube.
T	F	**8.**	A slow gauge reads less pressure than is actually in the boiler.
T	F	**9.**	Live steam allowed to enter the Bourdon tube of a steam pressure gauge will damage the gauge.
T	F	**10.**	The water column should be blown down once a shift.
T	F	**11.**	The water column is used to indicate the water level in the blowdown tank.
T	F	**12.**	With the boiler at its NOWL, the gauge glass is approximately half full.
T	F	**13.**	The purpose of the water column is to reduce the turbulence of the boiler water to obtain a more accurate reading of the water level in the gauge glass.
T	F	**14.**	In low pressure steam boilers, two methods of determining water level are try cocks and gauge glasses.
T	F	**15.**	Gauge glasses are calibrated in pounds per square inch.
T	F	**16.**	With water at the NOWL, steam is discharged from the bottom try cock when it is opened.
T	F	**17.**	With water at the NOWL, the middle try cock discharges a mixture of water and steam when opened.

ASME CODE SYMBOL STAMP	Before 2013	2013 and After	SAFETY RELIEF VALVE

T   F   **18.** With water at the NOWL, water is discharged from the top try cock when opened.

T   F   **19.** If the top line to the gauge glass is closed or clogged, the glass will fill with water.

T   F   **20.** If the bottom line to the gauge glass is closed or clogged, the glass will be empty.

T   F   **21.** To ensure the lines to the gauge glass are clear, it is recommended that the gauge be blown down at least once a month.

T   F   **22.** The bottom blowdown line must be connected to the highest part of the steam side of the boiler.

T   F   **23.** A high surface tension on boiler water can lead to foaming.

T   F   **24.** Surface impurities are removed from the boiler by using the bottom blowdown valves.

T   F   **25.** Boilers equipped with a quick-opening valve and a slow-opening valve must have the quick-opening valve closest to the boiler.

T   F   **26.** Only watertube boilers have bottom blowdown valves.

T   F   **27.** A high water level in the boiler can lead to carryover.

T   F   **28.** When dumping a boiler, there should be maximum steam pressure in the boiler to force water from the boiler.

T   F   **29.** To correct a high water level condition in the boiler, the operator can open the bottom blowdown valve.

T   F   **30.** Bottom blowdown valves are used when dumping the boiler.

T   F   **31.** A fusible plug is the last warning the operator has of a dangerous low-water condition in the boiler.

T   F   **32.** The core of the fusible plug melts at approximately 450°F.

T   F   **33.** The boiler vent is located at the highest part of the steam side of the boiler.

T   F   **34.** The safety valve should be used as a boiler vent for faster blowdown.

T   F   **35.** The boiler vent should be open when filling the boiler with water.

T   F   **36.** The pressure control is located at the highest part of the steam side of the boiler.

T   F   **37.** The pressure control must be mounted in a vertical position to ensure accurate operation.

T   F   **38.** A burner should always start up in high fire to ensure enough fuel for ignition.

T   F   **39.** Burners using fuel oil or gas should be adjusted so they are OFF for longer periods than they are ON to save fuel and keep furnace temperatures lower.

T   F   **40.** The operating range is obtained by adjusting the differential pressure setting and either the cut-in pressure setting or the cut-out pressure setting on the pressure control.

Multiple Choice

_____ 1. The ___ is the most important valve on a boiler.
      A. main steam stop valve
      B. safety valve
      C. automatic nonreturn valve
      D. feedwater stop valve

_____ 2. The MAWP on a low pressure steam boiler is ___ psi.
      A. 10
      B. 15
      C. 20
      D. 30

_____ 3. Total force on a safety valve is equal to ___.
      A. area times diameter
      B. area times distance
      C. area times pressure
      D. MAWP times pressure

_____ 4. The ASME Code states that boilers with over ___ square feet of heating surface must have two or more safety valves.
      A. 200
      B. 300
      C. 400
      D. 500

_____ 5. The area of a safety valve 4″ in diameter is ___ square inches.
      A. 2.3562
      B. 3.1416
      C. 6.2832
      D. 12.5664

_____ 6. The only valve permitted between the safety valve and the boiler is the ___ valve.
      A. os&y gate
      B. os&y globe
      C. automatic nonreturn
      D. none of the above

_____ 7. The range of the pressure gauge should be ___ times the MAWP of the boiler.
      A. 1 to 2
      B. 1½ to 2
      C. 2 to 3
      D. 2½ to 3

_____ **8.** In most states, ___ safety valves are permitted on steam boilers.
     A. deadweight
     B. blowdown
     C. spring-loaded pop-off
     D. none of the above

_____ **9.** The total force on a safety valve 2½″ in diameter with a steam pressure of 15 psi is ___.
     A. 19.5
     B. 29.5
     C. 73.6
     D. 93.8

_____ **10.** The steam pressure gauge on the boiler is calibrated to read ___.
     A. inches of vacuum
     B. pounds per square inch
     C. absolute pressure
     D. pressure below atmospheric pressure

_____ **11.** Steam is prevented from entering the Bourdon tube of the pressure gauge by a(n) ___.
     A. automatic nonreturn valve
     B. inspector's test cock
     C. os&y valve
     D. siphon

_____ **12.** A ___ pressure gauge can read either vacuum or pressure.
     A. compound
     B. duplex
     C. suction
     D. vacuum

_____ **13.** Vacuum is pressure ___ pressure.
     A. above gauge
     B. below absolute
     C. below atmospheric
     D. equal to gauge

_____ **14.** Safety valves are designed to pop open and stay open until there is a(n) ___ psi drop in pressure.
     A. 0 to 1
     B. 2 to 4
     C. 5 to 15
     D. over 15

_____ **15.** Safety valves are used on ___ boilers.
     A. firetube
     B. watertube
     C. cast iron
     D. all of the above

_____ **16.** The water column is located at the NOWL of a low pressure steam boiler, so the lowest visible part of the gauge glass is ___ above the lowest permissible water level recommended by the boiler manufacturer.
    A. 1″
    B. 4″ to 5″
    C. just
    D. never

_____ **17.** Blowback is the ___ in the boiler after the safety valve has opened.
    A. drop in pressure
    B. carryover
    C. increase of pressure
    D. chattering of a feedwater valve

_____ **18.** The boiler bottom blowdown line should discharge to a ___.
    A. blowdown separator
    B. blowdown tank
    C. heat exchanger
    D. all of the above

_____ **19.** If the desired cut-in pressure of the boiler is 6 psi and the desired cut-out pressure is 10 psi, the differential pressure setting must be ___ psi.
    A. 2
    B. 4
    C. 6
    D. 8

_____ **20.** Impurities that build up on the surface of the water in the boiler prevent ___ from breaking through the surface of the water.
    A. air
    B. oxygen
    C. CO_2
    D. steam

_____ **21.** To prevent air pressure from building up in the boiler when filling the boiler with water, the ___ must be open.
    A. safety valve
    B. main steam stop valve
    C. boiler vent
    D. manhole cover

_____ **22.** To prevent a vacuum from forming when taking the boiler off-line, the ___ must be open when pressure is still on the boiler.
    A. safety valve
    B. main steam stop valve
    C. boiler vent
    D. manhole cover

_____ **23.** The operating range of the boiler is controlled by the ___.
   A. aquastat
   B. vaporstat
   C. pressure control
   D. modulating pressure control

_____ **24.** The ___ regulates the firing rate between high and low fire of the burner.
   A. aquastat
   B. vaporstat
   C. pressure control
   D. modulating pressure control

_____ **25.** The best time to blow down a boiler to remove sludge and sediment is when the boiler is under a ___.
   A. high load
   B. light load
   C. load twice the MAWP
   D. maximum load

_____ **26.** The level of the water in the ___ indicates the water level in the boiler.
   A. condensate return tank
   B. try cocks
   C. gauge glass
   D. blowdown tank

_____ **27.** When blowing down a boiler, the quick-opening valve should always be opened ___ and closed ___.
   A. first; first
   B. first; last
   C. last; first
   D. last; last

_____ **28.** ___ added to boiler water change(s) scale-forming salts into a nonadhering sludge.
   A. Oxygen
   B. Minerals
   C. Slag
   D. Chemicals

_____ **29.** A ___ provides access inside the water side of the boiler for inspection, sight, or cleaning.
   A. boiler vent
   B. safety valve
   C. handhole
   D. siphon

_____ **30.** A(n) ___ gauge is a pressure gauge that reads more pressure than is actually in the boiler.
    A. broken
    B. slow
    C. uncalibrated
    D. fast

_____ **31.** According to the ASME Code, a try lever test on safety valves should be performed every ___ the boiler is in operation.
    A. hour
    B. four hours
    C. seven days
    D. 30 days

_____ **32.** The purpose of a safety valve is to prevent the pressure in the boiler from ___.
    A. exceeding the MAWP
    B. dropping below the MAWP
    C. causing a furnace explosion
    D. relieving water pressure

_____ **33.** The capacity of a safety valve is measured by the amount of steam that can be discharged per ___.
    A. shift
    B. hour
    C. minute
    D. day

_____ **34.** ___ is when a safety valve opens and closes rapidly.
    A. Depressurizing
    B. Pressurizing
    C. Chattering
    D. Huddling

_____ **35.** The safety valve on a low pressure boiler is designed to open when pressure in the boiler exceeds ___.
    A. the safety valve setting
    B. the NOWL
    C. feedwater pump pressure
    D. the bottom blowdown discharge pressure

_____ **36.** After the total force of the steam has lifted the safety valve off its seat, steam enters the ___.
    A. huddling chamber
    B. combustion chamber
    C. steam holding tank
    D. main steam line

_____ **37.** ___ causes false water level readings in the gauge glass.
      A. Priming
      B. Carryover
      C. Foaming
      D. Blowing down the boiler

_____ **38.** A ___ is an auxiliary device commonly used with boilers to transfer heat from a hotter fluid to a cooler fluid.
      A. heat exchanger
      B. blowdown tank
      C. blowdown attemperator
      D. steam trap

_____ **39.** On an additive pressure control, ___ pressure plus ___ pressure equals ___ pressure.
      A. differential; cut-out; cut-in
      B. cut-in; differential; cut-out
      C. cut-in; cut-out; differential
      D. cut-in; sequential; modulating

_____ **40.** A burner should always start up in ___ fire and shut down in ___ fire.
      A. low; low
      B. low; high
      C. high; low
      D. high; high

Safety Valve

_____ **1.** Valve disc

_____ **2.** Body

_____ **3.** Try lever pin

_____ **4.** Try lever

_____ **5.** Spindle

_____ **6.** Spring

_____ **7.** Valve seat

_____ **8.** Bonnet

Safety Valve Huddling Chamber

_____ **1.** Valve seat

_____ **2.** Huddling chamber

_____ **3.** Spring

_____ **4.** Valve spindle

_____ **5.** Steam pressure

_____ **6.** Valve disc

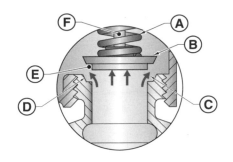

Steam Pressure Gauge Operation

_____ **1.** Linkage

_____ **2.** Siphon connection

_____ **3.** Steam pressure

_____ **4.** Face

_____ **5.** Needle

_____ **6.** Bourdon tube

_____ **7.** Case

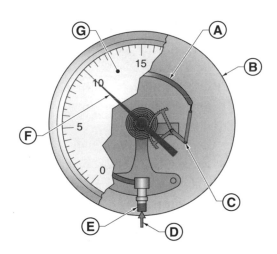

Water Column and Gauge Glass

_____ **1.** Water column

_____ **2.** Water column blowdown valve

_____ **3.** Cross tees

_____ **4.** Vent

_____ **5.** Try cocks

_____ **6.** Isolation valve

_____ **7.** Gauge glass

_____ **8.** NOWL

_____ **9.** Gauge glass blowdown valve

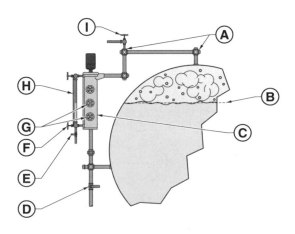

Bottom Blowdown Valve

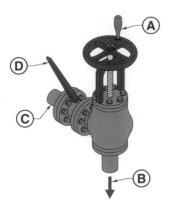

_____ **1.** Quick-opening valve

_____ **2.** Slow-opening valve

_____ **3.** To blowdown line

_____ **4.** From boiler

Additional Activities

1. Review Chapter 2 of *Low Pressure Boilers.*

2. Take the Quick Quiz® for Chapter 2 on the *Low Pressure Boilers* Interactive CD-ROM.

3. Review the following related Media Clips on the *Low Pressure Boilers* Interactive CD-ROM:
   - Bottom Blowdown
   - Gauge Glass
   - Gauge Glass Blowdown
   - Gauge Glass Replacement
   - High Water
   - Low Water
   - Pigtail Siphons
   - Safety Valves
   - Water Column

4. Review the Flash Cards for Chapter 2 on the *Low Pressure Boilers* Interactive CD-ROM.

5. Optionally, review the Master Math® Applications, Unit 1 to Unit 4, located on the *Low Pressure Boilers* Interactive CD-ROM. A link to a PDF document, Boiler Math Formulas, is provided on the Master Math® Applications home page.

Name _____ **Date** _____

True-False

T F **1.** A high water level condition in the boiler could lead to water hammer.

T F **2.** A low water level condition in the boiler can result in damage to boiler heating surfaces.

T F **3.** The check valve on the feedwater line should be located closest to the shell of the boiler.

T F **4.** The check valve allows the flow of water in one direction only.

T F **5.** The check valve on the feedwater line commonly has a valve disc that swings to open and close the valve.

T F **6.** A condensate return tank collects condensate returned from heating units for use in the boiler.

T F **7.** A globe valve used as a feedwater stop valve must be installed so inlet pressure is applied from under the valve disc.

T F **8.** The stop valve on the feedwater line should be located closest to the boiler.

T F **9.** The vacuum pump is designed to discharge air and pump water.

T F **10.** Centrifugal feedwater pumps are commonly driven by steam.

T F **11.** A check valve is opened by turning the handle counterclockwise.

T F **12.** A low water fuel cutoff is located slightly below the NOWL.

T F **13.** The range of pressure on the vacuum switch on a vacuum pump is usually 2″ to 8″.

T F **14.** An evaporation test is performed by opening the low water fuel cutoff blowdown valve by hand.

T F **15.** Any loss of water in the system must be made up by the makeup water feeder.

T F **16.** The boiler operator must be present during an evaporation test.

T F **17.** The makeup water feeder can be used as a feedwater regulator.

ASME CODE SYMBOL STAMP	Before 2013	2013 and After	POWER BOILER

T   F   **18.** Most makeup water contains some scale-forming salts.

T   F   **19.** The function of the automatic makeup water feeder is to replace water that has been lost.

T   F   **20.** The automatic city water makeup water feeder is located slightly below the NOWL.

Multiple Choice

_____ **1.** The water in a boiler is heated, turns to steam, and leaves the boiler through the ___.
    A. feedwater line
    B. main header
    C. main steam line
    D. main branch line

_____ **2.** When steam releases heat in a heat exchanger, it turns to ___.
    A. low pressure steam
    B. condensate
    C. makeup water
    D. exhaust steam

_____ **3.** A ___ pump returns condensate from the system back to the boiler.
    A. fuel oil
    B. return
    C. gear
    D. vacuum

_____ **4.** A ___ valve allows the flow of water in one direction only.
    A. gate
    B. globe
    C. os&y
    D. check

_____ **5.** The feedwater ___ valve should be located as close to the shell of the boiler as practical.
    A. check
    B. stop
    C. nonreturn
    D. regulating

_____ **6.** A ___ after each heating unit allows condensate to pass through to the return line.
    A. check valve
    B. steam trap
    C. water trap
    D. nonreturn valve

_____ **7.** A ___ may be required on some boilers to remove oxygen and other gases.
    A. makeup water system
    B. pressure relief valve
    C. feedwater regulator
    D. feedwater heater

_____ **8.** The feedwater ___ valve opens and closes automatically.
    A. return
    B. bypass
    C. check
    D. equalizing

_____ **9.** The vacuum pump pumps water and discharges air to the ___.
    A. expansion tank
    B. compression tank
    C. return tank
    D. atmosphere

_____ **10.** The range of pressure on the vacuum switch is usually ___.
    A. 2 to 6 psi
    B. 6 to 12 psi
    C. 2″ to 8″
    D. 8″ to 12″

_____ **11.** The primary function of a low water fuel cutoff is to ___.
    A. remove sludge and sediment from the bottom of the boiler
    B. shut down the burner if the water level drops below the safe operating level
    C. stop the flow of city water supplied to the condensate return tank
    D. reduce water turbulence in the gauge glass

_____ **12.** Water added to the boiler to replace water lost due to leaks and blowing down is known as ___ water.
    A. extra
    B. makeup
    C. boiler
    D. feed

_____ **13.** Excessive use of cold city makeup water reduces overall boiler efficiency because the water must be ___ before use in the boiler.
    A. vented
    B. heated
    C. filtered
    D. reticulated

_____ **14.** An auxiliary low water fuel cutoff is installed ___.
    A. slightly above the NOWL
    B. slightly below the primary low water fuel cutoff
    C. at the highest point on the boiler
    D. on the feedwater line close to the boiler shell.

_____ **15.** The ___ shuts off the burner in the event of low water.
    A. low water alarm
    B. feedwater regulator
    C. low water fuel cutoff
    D. automatic low water feeder

_____ 16. Water is supplied to the condensate return tank by the ___ pump.
  A. vacuum
  B. condensate
  C. feedwater
  D. return

_____ 17. The feedwater regulator is located at the ___.
  A. boiler vent
  B. MAWP
  C. NOWL
  D. bottom blowdown line

_____ 18. The ___ maintains a constant water level in the boiler.
  A. gauge glass
  B. water column
  C. blowdown tank
  D. feedwater regulator

_____ 19. The low water fuel cutoff should be tested ___.
  A. daily
  B. monthly
  C. semiannually
  D. annually

_____ 20. The burner should be ___ when the low water fuel cutoff is blown down.
  A. off
  B. firing
  C. tagged out
  D. tested

Testing Low Water Fuel Cutoff

_____ 1. Burner

_____ 2. Float at NOWL position

_____ 3. Mercury switch

_____ 4. Burner control

_____ 5. Float chamber

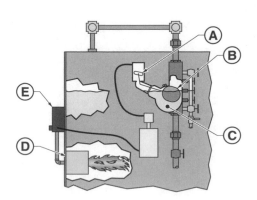

Feedwater System

_____	**1.** Boiler
_____	**2.** Check valve
_____	**3.** Condensate return line
_____	**4.** Condensate return tank
_____	**5.** Feedwater line
_____	**6.** Feedwater pump
_____	**7.** Heating unit

_____ **8.** Main steam header

_____ **9.** Main steam line

_____ **10.** Main steam stop valve

_____ **11.** Riser

_____ **12.** Stop valve

_____ **13.** Surge tank

_____ **14.** Steam trap

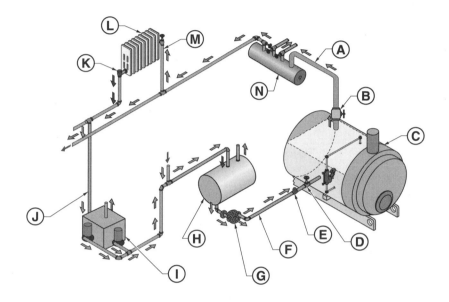

Makeup Water System

_____ **1.** Automatic makeup water feeder

_____ **2.** Backflow preventer

_____ **3.** Blowdown valves

_____ **4.** Burner

_____ **5.** Combination low water fuel cutoff/water column

_____ **6.** Condensate return line

_____ **7.** Makeup water supply

_____ **8.** Manual makeup water valve

_____ **9.** NOWL

_____ **10.** Strainer

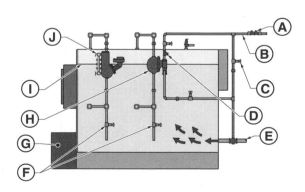

Feedwater Control

_____ **1.** Boiler

_____ **2.** Check valve

_____ **3.** Condensate return line

_____ **4.** Condensate return tank

_____ **5.** Feedwater pump

_____ **6.** NOWL

_____ **7.** Stop valve

_____ **8.** Surge tank

_____ **9.** Vent

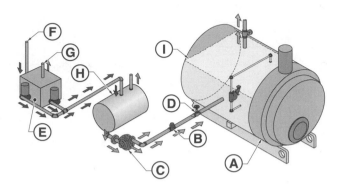

Feedwater Line

_____ **1.** Check valve

_____ **2.** Main feedwater line

_____ **3.** Boiler

_____ **4.** From feedwater heater

_____ **5.** Stop valve

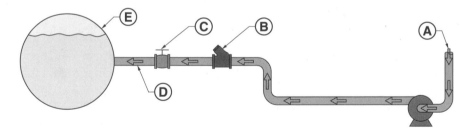

Vacuum Pump

_____ **1.** Condensate to boiler

_____ **2.** Vacuum tank

_____ **3.** Condensate from system

_____ **4.** Controls

_____ **5.** Vacuum switch

_____ **6.** Pump

_____ **7.** Float-controlled switches

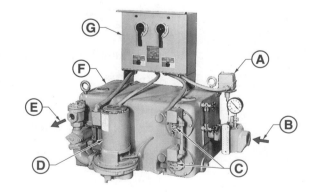

Centrifugal Water Pump

_____ 1. Feedwater to boiler

_____ 2. Housing

_____ 3. Inlet

_____ 4. Motor

_____ 5. Outlet

_____ 6. Rotating impeller

Low Water Fuel Cutoff Parts

_____ 1. Float

_____ 2. Water column

_____ 3. Control switches

_____ 4. Steam connection

_____ 5. Water connection

_____ 6. Float chamber

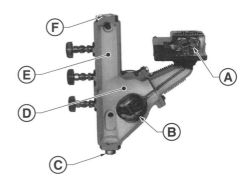

Low Water Fuel Cutoff Operation

_____ 1. Feedwater pump turns ON

_____ 2. Gauge glass

_____ 3. Burner shuts OFF

_____ 4. Gauge glass blowdown valve

_____ 5. Feedwater pump turns OFF

_____ 6. Lowest visible point in gauge glass

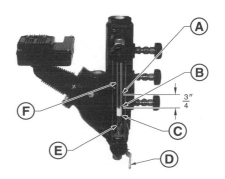

Additional Activities

1. Review Chapter 3 of *Low Pressure Boilers*.

2. Take the Quick Quiz® for Chapter 3 on the *Low Pressure Boilers* Interactive CD-ROM.

3. Review the following related Media Clips on the *Low Pressure Boilers* Interactive CD-ROM:
   • Centrifugal Pumps
   • Feedwater Check Valves
   • Feedwater Heaters
   • Low Water Fuel Cutoff

4. Review the Flash Cards for Chapter 3 on the *Low Pressure Boilers* Interactive CD-ROM.

5. Optionally, review the Master Math® Applications, Unit 7, located on the *Low Pressure Boilers* Interactive CD-ROM. A link to a PDF document, Boiler Math Formulas, is provided on the Master Math® Applications home page.

Name _____ Date _____

True-False

T   F   **1.** A nonreturn valve allows a boiler to be cut-in on-line or off-line automatically as the boiler pressure changes on startup or shutdown.

T   F   **2.** Heating units are designed to minimize heat loss from a building space.

T   F   **3.** A globe valve should never be used as a main steam stop valve.

T   F   **4.** Gate valves offer no restriction to flow when open.

T   F   **5.** A steam header is a distribution pipe that supplies steam to the branch lines.

T   F   **6.** A steam strainer should be located after a steam trap.

T   F   **7.** Steam traps are located throughout the system after each device where steam is used.

T   F   **8.** Expansion bends are used to route steam lines around obstacles.

T   F   **9.** Return steam traps discharge condensate directly back to the boiler.

T   F   **10.** Return steam traps are commonly found in modern boiler plants.

Multiple Choice

_____ **1.** Boiler main steam stop valves should be ___ valves.
     A. globe
     B. gate
     C. check
     D. safety

_____ **2.** Gate valves should always be ___ or ___ closed.
     A. partially open; completely
     B. wide open; partly
     C. wide open; completely
     D. throttled; completely

ASME CODE SYMBOL STAMP	Before 2013	2013 and After	SAFETY VALVE
	V	⟨ASME⟩ V	

_____ **3.** All boilers in battery must have two main steam stop valves or one main steam stop valve and one ___.
    A. steam trap
    B. expansion bend
    C. check valve
    D. automatic nonreturn valve

_____ **4.** When open, an os&y gate valve offers ___ to the flow of steam.
    A. no resistance
    B. throttling action
    C. velocity
    D. full resistance

_____ **5.** Steam traps are ___ devices.
    A. manual
    B. electrical
    C. automatic
    D. semiautomatic

_____ **6.** ___ allow movement caused from the heating and cooling of steam lines.
    A. Lagging valves
    B. Bottom blowdown valves
    C. Header baffles
    D. Expansion bends

_____ **7.** Steam traps remove ___ and ___ from the steam lines.
    A. air; water
    B. air; oil
    C. water; oil
    D. air; steam

_____ **8.** Condensate in the steam lines can result in ___.
    A. greater boiler efficiency
    B. pure steam production
    C. foaming
    D. water hammer

_____ **9.** A ___ valve is a type of globe valve that allows a boiler to be cut in on-line automatically when the boiler pressure is at or above the header pressure.
    A. return
    B. nonreturn
    C. test
    D. siphon

_____ **10.** ___ is jacketing material used to protect pipe insulation from mechanical damage.
  A. Lagging
  B. A baffle
  C. Steambound
  D. Header material

_____ **11.** Condensate from a nonreturn steam trap is pumped from the condensate return tank to the ___.
  A. return tank
  B. vacuum tank
  C. feedwater tank
  D. boiler

_____ **12.** Steam returning to the vacuum tank could cause the condensate pump to become ___.
  A. waterbound
  B. steambound
  C. waterlogged
  D. steamlogged

_____ **13.** Steam strainers should be located on the steam line ___.
  A. before the steam trap
  B. after the steam trap
  C. after the feedwater heater
  D. before the steam header

_____ **14.** A(n) ___ is a device used to test steam trap function by analyzing the sound waves emitted.
  A. infrared thermometer
  B. contact indicator
  C. sound flow indicator
  D. ultrasonic tester

_____ **15.** When an os&y valve is open, the stem is in the ___ position.
  A. floating
  B. locked
  C. up
  D. down

_____ **16.** A thermodynamic steam trap opens and closes by a(n) ___.
  A. float
  B. movable disc
  C. electric sensor
  D. flexible bellows

_____ **17.** In a float thermostatic trap, the float rises to discharge ___.
  A. condensate
  B. steam
  C. feedwater chemicals
  D. water and steam

_____ **18.** A steam trap that fails to open causes the heating unit to become ___.
      A. steambound
      B. waterlogged
      C. very hot
      D. contaminated with fuel oil

_____ **19.** ___ remove dirt and impurities that may cause the steam trap to malfunction.
      A. Vacuum pumps
      B. Globe valves
      C. Steam strainers
      D. Steam separators

_____ **20.** A(n) ___ is a device used to measure radiation emitted from an object.
      A. ultrasonic tester
      B. infrared thermometer
      C. contact thermometer
      D. radiant heater

Main Steam Stop Valve

_____ **1.** Main steam line

_____ **2.** Condensate

_____ **3.** Water level

_____ **4.** Steam trap

_____ **5.** Main steam stop valve

_____ **6.** Heating unit

_____ **7.** Steam

_____ **8.** Riser

_____ **9.** Main steam header

Steam Trap Operation

_____ **1.** Condensate discharge outlet

_____ **2.** Inverted bucket

_____ **3.** Discharge valve

_____ **4.** Steam and condensate inlet

_____ **5.** Steam and condensate inlet

_____ **6.** Movable disc closed position

_____ **7.** Trapped steam in control chamber

_____ **8.** Condensate discharge outlet

_____ **9.** Steam and condensate inlet

_____ **10.** Discharge valve

_____ **11.** Condensate discharge outlet

_____ **12.** Bellows

_____ **13.** Discharge valve

_____ **14.** Steam and condensate inlet

_____ **15.** Condensate discharge outlet

_____ **16.** Ball float

Steam Trap

_____ **1.** Thermodynamic

_____ **2.** Inverted bucket

_____ **3.** Thermostatic

_____ **4.** Float thermostatic

Steam Trap Location

_____ **1.** Feedwater pump

_____ **2.** Check valve

_____ **3.** Main steam line

_____ **4.** Steam trap

_____ **5.** Heating unit

_____ **6.** Stop valve

_____ **7.** Main steam stop valve

_____ **8.** Condensate return tank

_____ **9.** Strainer

_____ **10.** Main steam header

_____ **11.** Condensate return line

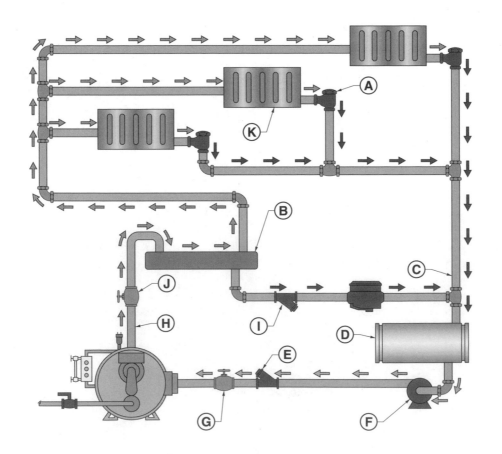

Steam Trap Testing Devices

_____ **1.** Contact thermometer

_____ **2.** Temperature-indicating crayon

_____ **3.** Flow indicator

_____ **4.** Ultrasonic tester

_____ **5.** Infrared thermometer

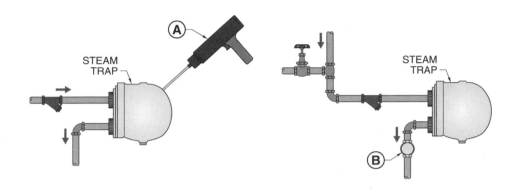

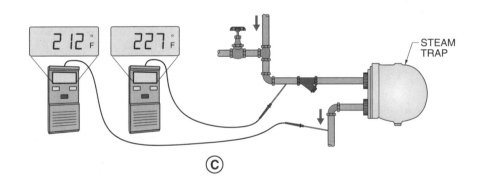

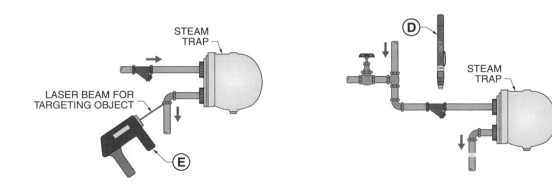

Testing Steam Traps

_____   **1.** Steam trap functioning normally

_____   **2.** Steam trap malfunction

_____   **3.** Strainer clogged

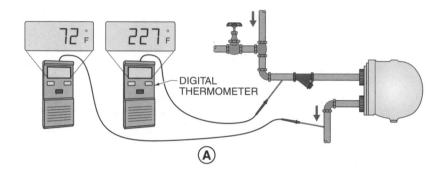

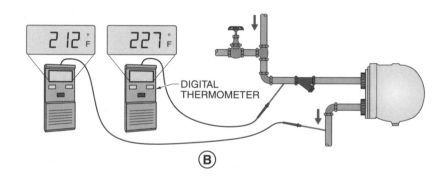

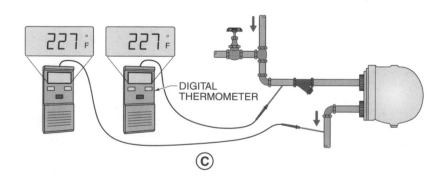

Additional Activities

1. Review Chapter 4 of *Low Pressure Boilers.*

2. Take the Quick Quiz® for Chapter 4 on the *Low Pressure Boilers* Interactive CD-ROM.

3. Review the following related Media Clips on the *Low Pressure Boilers* Interactive CD-ROM:
   • OS&Y Steam Valves
   • Steam System
   • Steam Traps
   • Steam Trap Troubleshooting

4. Review the Flash Cards for Chapter 4 on the *Low Pressure Boilers* Interactive CD-ROM.

5. Optionally, review the Master Math® Applications, Unit 5 to Unit 6, located on the *Low Pressure Boilers* Interactive CD-ROM. A link to a PDF document, Boiler Math Formulas, is provided on the Master Math® Applications home page.

Name _____ Date _____

True-False

T	F	**1.**	Fuel oil and gas are the most commonly used fuels in low pressure boilers.
T	F	**2.**	The fire point temperature is higher than the flash point temperature.
T	F	**3.**	A fuel oil relief valve is located between the fuel oil pump and the fuel oil discharge valve.
T	F	**4.**	The fuel oil pump should be started with its discharge valve open.
T	F	**5.**	Cold fuel oil in the tank will give a high suction reading.
T	F	**6.**	A dirty strainer results in low suction readings.
T	F	**7.**	Starting the fuel oil pump with its discharge valve closed causes the relief valve to open.
T	F	**8.**	Fuel oil burners commonly use atomizing burners.
T	F	**9.**	Rotary cup burners can burn only No. 2 fuel oil.
T	F	**10.**	Rotary cup burners atomize fuel oil using a spinning cup and high-velocity air.
T	F	**11.**	Air used to atomize fuel oil is primary air.
T	F	**12.**	Secondary air is needed to burn the fuel oil efficiently.
T	F	**13.**	In an air atomizing burner, steam and fuel are discharged to the burner for combustion.
T	F	**14.**	The air atomizing burner uses air to mix with the fuel oil to achieve a high degree of atomization.
T	F	**15.**	Complete combustion is achieved in a burner by supplying the proper mixture of air and fuel to the furnace.
T	F	**16.**	In a rotary cup burner, the solenoid valve controls the flow of fuel through the fuel tube.

ASME CODE SYMBOL STAMP	Before 2013	2013 and After PP	PRESSURE PIPING

T   F   **17.** Fuel oil to be removed from the burner nozzle is purged with air.

T   F   **18.** A metal scraper is used to clean deposits on a fuel oil burner nozzle.

T   F   **19.** In a low pressure gas system, before the manual reset valve can be opened, the pilot must be lit.

T   F   **20.** The manual reset valve in the gas system closes if the boiler has a high water level.

T   F   **21.** A fuel oil heater is required when using No. 2 fuel oil.

T   F   **22.** Fuel oil is a liquid fossil fuel.

T   F   **23.** Plant flexibility is increased with the use of a combination burner.

T   F   **24.** Anthracite coal is hard coal.

T   F   **25.** Hard coal has a high volatile content.

T   F   **26.** Bituminous coal is soft coal.

T   F   **27.** Boilers burning soft coal need large furnace volumes to complete combustion.

T   F   **28.** Gases of combustion that contact boiler heating surfaces before combustion is completed cause soot and smoke.

T   F   **29.** Grates are only needed in hand-fired coal boilers to support the coal.

T   F   **30.** Smoke is a sign of incomplete combustion.

T   F   **31.** Smoke is less of a problem when burning hard coal as compared to soft coal.

T   F   **32.** Stokers were developed to reduce the amount of coal fed to the furnace.

T   F   **33.** Stoker firing allowed the design of larger coal-fired boilers.

T   F   **34.** The type of fuel used determines the fuel system accessories required.

T   F   **35.** Purging the lines and nozzles of an air atomizing burner at the end of its firing cycle keeps lines and nozzles clean for the next starting cycle.

T   F   **36.** Natural gas is a colorless and odorless fossil fuel.

T   F   **37.** Propane is lighter than air and requires special handling.

T   F   **38.** The viscosity of fuel oil is the temperature at which it will burn continually when exposed to an open flame.

T   F   **39.** The flash point of fuel oil is the temperature at which it will resist burning.

T   F   **40.** It is best to burn fuel oil with a low flash point.

T   F   **41.** Pour point is the lowest temperature at which fuel oil will flow as a liquid.

T   F   **42.** A therm is the quantity of gas required to produce 100,000 Btu.

T   F   **43.** The temperature of No. 6 fuel in a fuel oil tank should be maintained at approximately 100°F to 120°F.

T   F   **44.** Fuel oil in the storage tank must be kept below its flash point temperature.

T   F   **45.** The temperature of the fuel oil in the storage tank must be kept above the recommended pour point.

T   F   **46.** No. 6 fuel oil must be heated to the proper temperature in order to burn.

T   F   **47.** The flame scanner proves the main flame only.

T   F   **48.** The furnace must be purged after any flame failure.

Multiple Choice

_____ **1.** When burning No. 6 fuel oil, the fuel oil strainers should be cleaned at least once every ___ hr.
    A. 8
    B. 10
    C. 12
    D. 24

_____ **2.** When cleaning a fuel oil strainer, the ___ must be carefully replaced to prevent air from entering the system.
    A. plug valve
    B. gasket
    C. hand screw
    D. basket

_____ **3.** The ___ pump draws fuel oil from the fuel oil tank.
    A. transfer
    B. fuel oil
    C. condensate
    D. circulating

_____ **4.** The ___ valve protects the fuel lines and pump from excessive pressure.
    A. safety
    B. bypass
    C. relief
    D. stop

_____ **5.** A high vacuum on the fuel oil suction gauge normally indicates ___.
    A. low viscosity or clogged vent
    B. a closed discharge valve or hot fuel oil
    C. cold fuel oil or a dirty strainer
    D. water in the fuel oil or a worn pump

_____ **6.** Fuel oil burners are designed to provide fuel oil to the furnace in a ___.
    A. steady stream
    B. fine spray
    C. half spray, half stream
    D. none of the above

_____ 7. The rotary cup burner uses ___ to atomize the fuel oil.
    A. high temperature steam and pressure
    B. high temperature air and pressure
    C. steam and No. 6 fuel oil
    D. a spinning cup and high-velocity air

_____ 8. In a low pressure gas burner, gas is mixed with air in the ___.
    A. burner
    B. mixing chamber before the burner register
    C. combustion chamber
    D. boiler furnace

_____ 9. In a high pressure gas burner, the gas mixes with the air on the inside of the ___.
    A. burner
    B. mixing chamber
    C. combustion chamber
    D. boiler furnace

_____ 10. A ___ is a narrowed portion of a tube.
    A. solenoid
    B. butterfly valve
    C. venturi
    D. pilot regulator

_____ 11. On a low pressure gas system, the manual reset cannot be opened until the ___.
    A. vaporstat proves pressure
    B. boiler is vented
    C. pilot is lit
    D. all of the above

_____ 12. ___ coal is hard coal.
    A. Lignite
    B. Anthracite
    C. Bituminous
    D. High-volatile

_____ 13. In a high pressure gas system, the plant pressure ___ valve reduces gas pressure to line pressure used in the system.
    A. butterfly
    B. regulating
    C. safety
    D. pilot

_____ 14. ___ coal is coal that is ground to a fine powder.
    A. Anthracite
    B. Bituminous
    C. Pulverized
    D. none of the above

_____ **15.** A ___ is a mechanical device for feeding coal consistently to the burner.
- A. grate burner
- B. stoker
- C. hopper shoveler
- D. all of the above

_____ **16.** A(n) ___ is an air pressure-activated switch that closes after proving sufficient pressure of combustion air from the forced draft fan.
- A. air proving switch
- B. pilot modulating relay
- C. combustion flowmeter
- D. pressure switch control

_____ **17.** A combination burner allows the operator to switch fuels ___.
- A. for economy
- B. if there is a shortage of a fuel
- C. if there is a failure in the fuel system being used
- D. all of the above

_____ **18.** Hard coal is ___.
- A. bituminous coal with a high carbon content
- B. bituminous coal with a high volatile content
- C. anthracite coal with a high volatile content
- D. anthracite coal with a high carbon content

_____ **19.** Soft coal is ___.
- A. bituminous coal with a high carbon content
- B. bituminous coal with a high volatile content
- C. anthracite coal with a high volatile content
- D. anthracite coal with a high carbon content

_____ **20.** A(n) ___ sensor senses light frequencies that are higher than those visible to the eye.
- A. photocell
- B. infrared
- C. ultraviolet
- D. all of the above

_____ **21.** A(n) ___ is a safety device that senses if the pilot light and/or main flame are lit.
- A. low water fuel cutoff
- B. annunciator
- C. flame scanner
- D. none of the above

_____ **22.** The ___ of fuel oil is the lowest temperature at which it will flow as a liquid.
- A. fire point
- B. flash point
- C. pour point
- D. viscosity

_____ 23. The ___ of fuel oil is the temperature at which fuel oil gives off vapor that flashes when exposed to an open flame.
    A. fire point
    B. flash point
    C. pour point
    D. viscosity

_____ 24. The ___ is the temperature at which fuel oil will burn continuously when exposed to an open flame.
    A. fire point
    B. flash point
    C. pour point
    D. viscosity

_____ 25. The internal resistance of fuel oil to flow is the ___.
    A. fire point
    B. flash point
    C. pour point
    D. viscosity

_____ 26. In order to reduce the viscosity of fuel oil, it is necessary to ___.
    A. decrease its temperature
    B. decrease its pour point
    C. increase its temperature
    D. decrease its pressure

_____ 27. A leak on the fuel oil suction line between the tank and the suction side of the fuel oil pump would result in ___.
    A. the suction gauge pulsating
    B. air entering the suction line
    C. pulsating of the fire in the boiler
    D. all of the above

_____ 28. Stokers were developed to ___.
    A. increase the efficiency of burning coal
    B. keep furnace temperatures constant
    C. allow for development of larger coal-fired boilers
    D. all of the above

_____ 29. Foreign matter in the coal hopper of the screw-feed stoker is best removed by ___.
    A. emptying the coal hopper
    B. reversing the stoker
    C. forcing it through with a heavy shear pin
    D. using the cutoff gate at the bottom of the hopper

_____ **30.** A ___ is used to prevent damage to the transmission of a screw-feed stoker in the event of an obstruction clogging the feed screw.
    A. slip clutch
    B. fuse
    C. shear pin or key
    D. none of the above

_____ **31.** In order to bank a fire, the ___ is disengaged.
    A. combination fan
    B. coal feed
    C. feedwater
    D. boiler stop valve

_____ **32.** In a screw-feed stoker, a(n) ___ draft fan supplies air for combustion.
    A. induced
    B. combination
    C. forced
    D. natural

_____ **33.** To prevent smoke and to aid in complete combustion in the screw-feed stoker, ___ air is provided using a separate damper control.
    A. underfire
    B. overfire
    C. retort
    D. grate zone

_____ **34.** The ram-feed stoker is a(n) ___ stoker.
    A. overfeed
    B. traveling grate
    C. side feed
    D. underfeed

_____ **35.** A(n) ___ system is a solid-state control system in which a building automation controller is wired directly to control devices.
    A. ultraviolet burner control (UBC)
    B. modulating control status (MCS)
    C. programmed emission safeguard (PES)
    D. direct digital control (DDC)

_____ **36.** ___ analysis is a chemical process used to determine the quantity of elements that a substance is composed of.
    A. Ultimate
    B. Flue-gas
    C. High-volatile
    D. all of the above

_____ **37.** A(n) ___ system is a combustion control system that controls the amount of steam produced by starting and stopping the boiler.
    A. modulating control
    B. ON/OFF control
    C. burner proving
    D. none of the above

_____ **38.** ___ combustion is the burning of all the fuel using the minimum amount of excess air.
    A. Incomplete
    B. Complete
    C. Perfect
    D. Imperfect

_____ **39.** ___ combustion occurs when the fuel is not all burned, resulting in formation of soot and smoke.
    A. Incomplete
    B. Complete
    C. Perfect
    D. Imperfect

_____ **40.** A(n) ___ is a combustion control system that controls the amount of steam produced by changing the burner firing rate.
    A. ON/OFF control system
    B. aquastat
    C. temperature flowmeter
    D. modulating control system

_____ **41.** A ___ is burner control equipment that monitors the burner start-up sequence and the main flame during normal operation.
    A. flame safeguard system
    B. flue gas analyzer
    C. modulation control system
    D. none of the above

_____ **42.** A ___ is a control that functions as the mastermind of the burner control system to control the firing cycle.
    A. pressure control
    B. butterfly solenoid
    C. programmer
    D. primary combustion analyzer

_____ **43.** A pollutant is matter that contaminates ___.
    A. air
    B. soil
    C. water
    D. all of the above

_____ **44.** ___ is the amount of fuel the burner is capable of burning in a given unit of time.
    A. High fire
    B. Low fire
    C. Firing rate
    D. Heating surface

45. ___ is the black residue formed when unburned coal in the combustion gases sticks to the boiler's tube surface.

    A. Soot

    B. Sulfur dioxide

    C. Carbon monoxide

    D. Secondary air

46. ___ fire is burning the maximum amount of fuel in a given unit of time.

    A. Low

    B. High

    C. Maximum

    D. Medium

47. Combustion controls regulate ___.

    A. fuel supply in proportion to steam demand

    B. air supply

    C. ratio of air to the fuel supplied

    D. all of the above

48. ___ air controls the amount of fuel oil capable of being burned.

    A. Forced

    B. Primary

    C. Secondary

    D. all of the above

49. ___ air controls the combustion efficiency.

    A. Forced

    B. Primary

    C. Secondary

    D. all of the above

50. When the flame safeguard sequences the burner function, ___ is the period of time during which the pilot and main burner must be lit.

    A. prepurge

    B. pilot flame-establishing period

    C. ignition trials

    D. postpurge

51. Unburned fuel in a gaseous state is removed from the furnace by ___.

    A. vacuum pumps

    B. purging the furnace

    C. burning the fuel

    D. all of the above

52. Unburned fuel oil that is heated in the furnace will ___.

    A. turn into steam

    B. vaporize

    C. solidify

    D. flow slowly

_____ **53.** A photocell sensor senses ___ light.
      A. infrared
      B. ultraviolet
      C. visible
      D. all of the above

_____ **54.** The flame scanner proves the ___ and main flame.
      A. pilot
      B. combustion air
      C. high fire valve
      D. stack flame

_____ **55.** Well-designed burners firing gaseous and liquid fuels operate at excess air levels of approximately ___%.
      A. 0.433
      B. 15
      C. 25
      D. 212

_____ **56.** The ___ of a modulating burner is the ratio of the maximum firing rate to the minimum firing rate.
      A. firing rate
      B. burning ratio
      C. maximizer rate
      D. turndown ratio

_____ **57.** ___ is the condition where a flame travels upwind and into the burner assembly.
      A. Blowdown
      B. Blowback
      C. Flashdown
      D. Flashback

_____ **58.** The primary function of the boiler management and control system is ___.
      A. low water protection
      B. combustion safety
      C. controlling high water
      D. none of the above

_____ **59.** ___ are pollution standards for six priority polletants set by the Environmental Protection Agency through the Clean Air Act.
      A. PLCs
      B. BMCS
      C. EPAQS
      D. NAAQS

_____ **60.** When an increase in steam pressure is required, the ___ activates the programmer to start the firing cycle.
      A. aquastat
      B. remote sensor
      C. pressure control
      D. pressure gauge

Fuel Oil Pump

_____ **1.** Crescent seal

_____ **2.** Shaft

_____ **3.** Suction side

_____ **4.** Drive gear

_____ **5.** Ring gear

_____ **6.** Discharge side

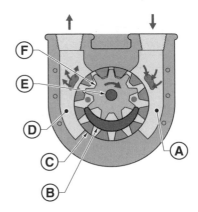

Low Pressure Gas System

_____ **1.** Butterfly valve

_____ **2.** Gas pressure switch

_____ **3.** Gas burner

_____ **4.** Main gas shutoff cock

_____ **5.** Pilot shutoff cock

_____ **6.** Blower

_____ **7.** Gas pilot

_____ **8.** Manual reset valve

_____ **9.** Mixing chamber

_____ **10.** Gas supply line

_____ **11.** Main gas solenoid valve

_____ **12.** Pilot solenoid valve

_____ **13.** Venturi

_____ **14.** Gas pressure regulator

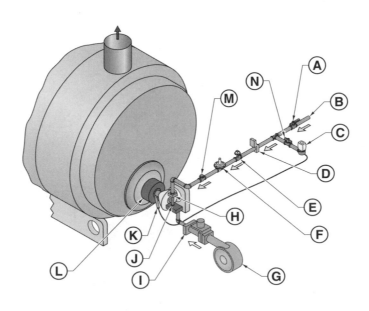

Screw-Feed Stoker

_____ **1.** Feed screw

_____ **2.** Apron

_____ **3.** Cutoff gate

_____ **4.** Pusher block

_____ **5.** Motor

_____ **6.** Extension

_____ **7.** Retort

_____ **8.** Transmission

_____ **9.** Hopper

_____ **10.** Dumping grates

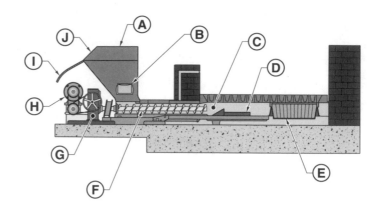

High Pressure Gas System

_____ **1.** Utility meter

_____ **2.** Pilot vent valve

_____ **3.** Main gas vent valve

_____ **4.** Pilot adjusting cock

_____ **5.** Utility pressure regulating valve

_____ **6.** Low gas pressure switch

_____ **7.** Butterfly gas valve

_____ **8.** Pilot pressure regulator

_____ **9.** Pilot valves

_____ **10.** Pilot pressure gauge

_____ **11.** Main gas shutoff cock

_____ **12.** Pilot shutoff cock

_____ **13.** Main gas valve

_____ **14.** Plant pressure regulating valve

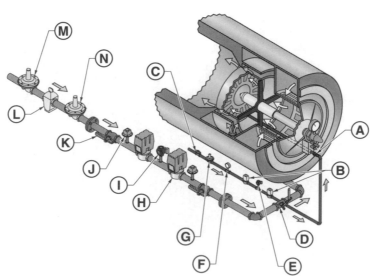

Ram-Feed Stoker

_____ **1.** Blower

_____ **2.** Air chamber

_____ **3.** Retort chamber

_____ **4.** Grate bars

_____ **5.** Auxiliary pusher blocks

_____ **6.** Fuel bed

_____ **7.** Hopper

_____ **8.** Feeder block

_____ **9.** Sliding bottom

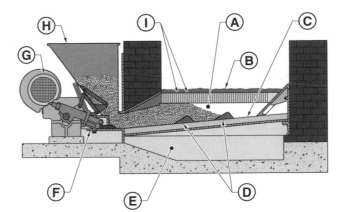

Fuel Oil Burner

_____ **1.** Rotary cup

_____ **2.** Air atomizing

_____ **3.** Pressure atomizing

_____ **4.** Steam atomizing

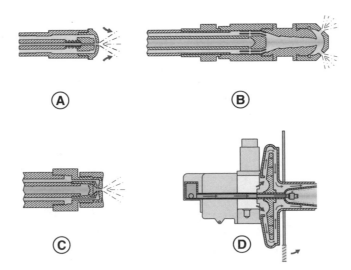

Modulating Control

_____ 1. Bellows

_____ 2. Pressure setting

_____ 3. To siphon

_____ 4. Differential setting

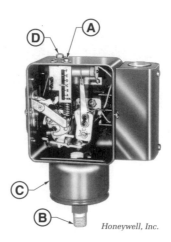

Honeywell, Inc.

Fuel Oil System

_____ 1. Vacuum gauge

_____ 2. Fuel oil relief valve

_____ 3. Nozzle air pressure gauge

_____ 4. Fuel oil controller

_____ 5. Fuel oil strainer

_____ 6. Modulating cam

_____ 7. Fuel oil burner pressure gauge

_____ 8. Check valve

_____ 9. Fuel oil thermometer

_____ 10. Metering valve

_____ 11. Main fuel oil solenoid valves

_____ 12. Fuel oil pressure gauge

_____ 13. Fuel oil pump

_____ 14. Fuel oil pressure regulator

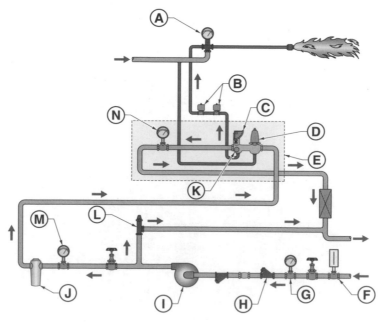

Flame Sensor

_____ **1.** Ultraviolet

_____ **2.** Flame rod

_____ **3.** Infrared

_____ **4.** Photocell

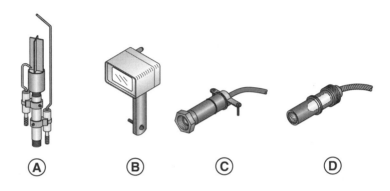

Fuel Oil Strainer

_____ **1.** Strainer basket

_____ **2.** Basket housing

_____ **3.** Hand screw

_____ **4.** Drain plug

_____ **5.** Plug valve

_____ **6.** Handle position indicates basket in service

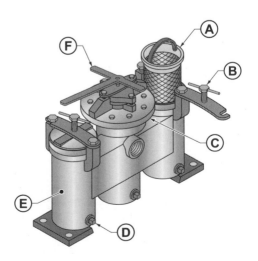

Additional Activities

1. Review Chapter 5 of *Low Pressure Boilers*.

2. Take the Quick Quiz® for Chapter 5 on the *Low Pressure Boilers* Interactive CD-ROM.

3. Review the following related Media Clips on the *Low Pressure Boilers* Interactive CD-ROM:
   • Combination Burners
   • Dampers
   • Flame Scanners
   • Fuel Heating Value
   • Fuel Oil Level Gauges
   • Stokers

4. Review the Flash Cards for Chapter 5 on the *Low Pressure Boilers* Interactive CD-ROM.

Name _____ **Date** _____

True-False

T   F   **1.** Draft is the difference in pressure between two points that causes air or gases of combustion to flow.

T   F   **2.** Gases move from an area of low pressure to an area of high pressure.

T   F   **3.** The two types of draft are mechanical and forced.

T   F   **4.** Mechanical draft is produced by a fan or blower.

T   F   **5.** Air is necessary for combustion process to take place.

T   F   **6.** Dampers can be used to control the flow of air and gases of combustion.

T   F   **7.** Approximately 75 lb of air is required for every pound of fuel burned.

T   F   **8.** The amount of natural draft generated is affected by the height of the chimney.

T   F   **9.** The two types of mechanical draft are forced and induced.

T   F   **10.** The induced draft fan is located on the front of the boiler.

T   F   **11.** A variable-speed drive (VSD) is a motor controller used to vary the frequency of the electrical signal supplied to an AC motor.

T   F   **12.** Balanced draft is a mechanical draft from fans located before and after the boiler.

T   F   **13.** The forced draft fan is located in the breeching.

T   F   **14.** Some boilers have combination forced and induced draft fans.

T   F   **15.** Draft is typically measured in pounds per square inch (psi).

T   F   **16.** A cool stack condition can result in condensation of water vapor in the gases of combustion.

T   F   **17.** Natural draft produces greater amounts of draft in the winter than in the summer.

ASME CODE SYMBOL STAMP	Before 2013	2013 and After	**BOILER ASSEMBLY**

    T   F   **18.** When using a manometer to measure draft, the liquid level in one leg is compared to the liquid level in the other leg.

    T   F   **19.** Proper control of draft results in higher combustion efficiency.

    T   F   **20.** The amount of draft determines the rate of combustion.

Multiple Choice

_____ **1.** The induced draft fan is located in the ___.
    A. boiler room
    B. breeching
    C. chimney
    D. fan room

_____ **2.** The amount of natural draft present can be affected by ___.
    A. dampers opened or closed
    B. temperature of the gases of combustion
    C. height of the chimney
    D. all of the above

_____ **3.** Draft is the difference in pressure between two points that causes ___ to flow.
    A. air
    B. natural gas
    C. steam
    D. all of the above

_____ **4.** A ___ is a steel chimney used to direct the flow of gases of combustion from the boiler to the atmosphere.
    A. damper tube
    B. tube sheet
    C. refractory assembly
    D. stack

_____ **5.** Forced draft and induced draft are two types of ___ draft.
    A. natural
    B. mechanical
    C. induced
    D. all of the above

_____ **6.** Mechanical draft is produced by ___.
    A. a chimney
    B. power-driven fans
    C. temperature difference
    D. all of the above

_____ **7.** ___ draft is air that is pulled through the boiler.
    A. Induced
    B. Forced
    C. Combination
    D. Natural

_____ **8.** ___ draft is produced when air is pushed through the burner.
    A. Induced
    B. Forced
    C. Combination
    D. Natural

_____ **9.** A ___ is a device used to create resistance in order to regulate the flow of air and gases of combustion in a boiler.
    A. regulator
    B. variable-speed drive
    C. fan
    D. damper

_____ **10.** By using ___ draft, higher rates of combustion can be achieved than with natural draft.
    A. mechanical
    B. automatic
    C. manufactured
    D. atmospheric

_____ **11.** Cold outside air affects the amount of ___ draft produced.
    A. induced
    B. forced
    C. combination
    D. natural

_____ **12.** Draft gauge measurements are expressed in inches of ___.
    A. mercury
    B. water column
    C. saturated steam
    D. all of the above

_____ **13.** A ___ is a simple draft gauge consisting of a U-shaped glass tube.
    A. pyrometer
    B. dynometer
    C. manometer
    D. trynometer

_____ **14.** When measuring draft in the breeching, one leg of the tube is open to the breeching and the other to the ___.
    A. windbox
    B. atmosphere
    C. forced draft fan
    D. induced draft fan

_____ **15.** Improperly burned fuel results in ___.
    A. soot and smoke
    B. high surface tension
    C. high combustion efficiency
    D. increased steam consumption

_____ **16.** High combustion efficiency produces the maximum amount of ___ generated by the fuel.
        A. carbon monoxide
        B. heat
        C. water
        D. ash

_____ **17.** Too much draft when burning coal may cause ___.
        A. too hot a fire
        B. low steam pressure
        C. high water
        D. reduced fuel consumption

_____ **18.** Combination forced and induced draft is also known as ___ draft.
        A. natural
        B. positive flow
        C. balanced
        D. forced natural

Manometer

_____ **1.** Positive reading

_____ **2.** No reading

_____ **3.** Negative reading

Natural Draft

_____ **1.** Cold air for combustion

_____ **2.** Hot gases of combustion

_____ **3.** Gases of combustion released to atmosphere

_____ **4.** Cold ambient air

_____ **5.** Chimney

_____ **6.** Heat

Forced Draft

_____ **1.** Forced draft fan

_____ **2.** Chimney

_____ **3.** Gases of combustion

_____ **4.** Air flow

_____ **5.** Boiler drum

_____ **6.** Outlet damper

_____ **7.** Furnace

_____ **8.** Air entering furnace

_____ **9.** Inlet damper

_____ **10.** Breeching

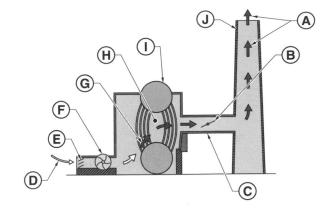

Draft Control

_____ **1.** Burner nozzle

_____ **2.** Blower motor

_____ **3.** Gases of combustion

_____ **4.** Outlet

_____ **5.** Forced draft fan

_____ **6.** Boiler

_____ **7.** Gas pilot assembly

_____ **8.** Intake

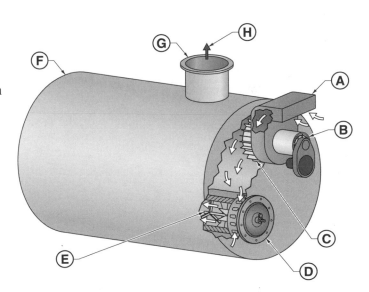

Stack

_____   **1.** Stack

_____   **2.** Boiler

_____   **3.** Drain connection

_____   **4.** Cleanout

_____   **5.** Forced draft fan

_____   **6.** Breeching

_____   **7.** Gases of combustion to atmosphere

_____   **8.** Outlet

_____   **9.** Offset stack

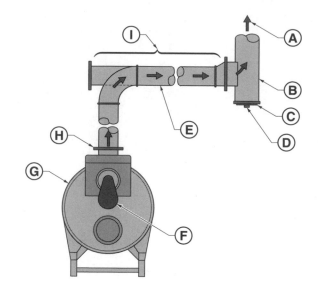

Additional Activities

1. Review Chapter 6 of *Low Pressure Boilers.*

2. Take the Quick Quiz® for Chapter 6 on the *Low Pressure Boilers* Interactive CD-ROM.

3. Review the following related Media Clips on the *Low Pressure Boilers* Interactive CD-ROM:
   • Dampers
   • Draft Types

4. Review the Flash Cards for Chapter 6 on the *Low Pressure Boilers* Interactive CD-ROM.

Name _____ Date _____

True-False

T   F   **1.** Boiler water treatment is required for makeup water introduced to the boiler.

T   F   **2.** Slug feeding is used to generate foam to prevent carryover.

T   F   **3.** Dissolved solids are impurities such as calcium, silica, and iron dissolved in solution.

T   F   **4.** Priming and carryover can lead to water hammer and possible pipe rupture.

T   F   **5.** Oxygen in the boiler water is used to remove nonadhering sludge.

T   F   **6.** Water that contains a small quantity of minerals is hard water.

T   F   **7.** Scale acts as an insulator and slows down the transfer of heat to the water.

T   F   **8.** Chemicals added to the boiler water change scale-forming salts into nonadhering sludge.

T   F   **9.** Sludge is removed from the boiler using the surface blowdown valve.

T   F   **10.** A boil-out procedure is performed when a new boiler is installed.

T   F   **11.** Well water requires chemical treatment but city water does not.

T   F   **12.** The bypass feeder is located on the main steam header to provide efficient feeding.

T   F   **13.** Priming and carryover can be caused by opening the main steam valve too quickly.

T   F   **14.** Corrosion is the accumulation of sludge on boiler heating surfaces.

T   F   **15.** Fuel oil contamination of the boiler water can be prevented by dumping all fuel oil heater returns to waste.

T   F   **16.** Scale and sediment cause pitting of the boiler metal surfaces.

T   F   **17.** Sodium sulfite is an oxygen scavenger that is commonly used to treat boiler water.

T   F   **18.** Automatic valves are used to control the amount of chemicals added by the bypass feeder.

ASME CODE SYMBOL STAMP	Before 2013	2013 and After	MINIATURE BOILER
	M	A S M E M	

T	F	**19.** Rusting of the boiler metal is caused by oxygen in the boiler water.
T	F	**20.** Sludge rises when the boiler is on light load and is removed using the try cocks on the water column at the NOWL.
T	F	**21.** Scale formation can result in an increase in fuel required to generate steam.
T	F	**22.** Boiler water treatment required for most low pressure boilers is minimal if the boiler recovers all or most of the condensate returns.
T	F	**23.** Water is cooled to reduce the amount of dissolved oxygen.
T	F	**24.** Fuel oil contamination of the boiler water most commonly occurs in plants using No. 2 fuel oil.
T	F	**25.** Oxygen in the boiler water can be removed by adding sodium sulfite.

Multiple Choice

_____ **1.** Water that contains large quantities of dissolved minerals is called ___.
   A. soft water
   B. hard water
   C. sludge
   D. sediment

_____ **2.** Small particles of water carried into steam lines are called ___.
   A. scale formation
   B. blistering
   C. carryover
   D. priming

_____ **3.** ___ is a condition caused when steam bubbles are trapped below the boiler water surface.
   A. Sludge slugging
   B. Foaming
   C. Priming
   D. Tube corrosion

_____ **4.** ___ is the exposure to highly alkaline elements, causing boiler metal corrosion at stress zones.
   A. Sodium sulfate
   B. Caustic embrittlement
   C. Corrosion
   D. Pitting

_____ **5.** ___ is used as an oxygen scavenger to remove oxygen from the boiler water.
   A. Sodium sulfite
   B. Zeolite
   C. Sodium sulfate
   D. none of the above

_____ **6.** Nonadhering sludge is best removed when the boiler is ___.
A. under light load
B. under heavy load
C. being drained
D. being tested

_____ **7.** Overheating of heating surfaces can result in ___.
A. bags
B. blisters
C. burned-out tubes
D. all of the above

_____ **8.** In low pressure boiler operation, chemicals for reducing oxygen and preventing scale can be added using a ___.
A. vacuum pump
B. blowdown valve
C. safety valve
D. bypass feeder

_____ **9.** Scale is caused by ___.
A. scale-forming salts
B. hard water
C. mineral deposits
D. all of the above

_____ **10.** ___ in the boiler water causes corrosion and pitting of the boiler metal.
A. Sodium sulfite
B. Sodium sulfate
C. Carbon monoxide
D. Oxygen

_____ **11.** High surface tension on the boiler water is shown by ___.
A. pressure above 15 psi
B. steam released by the top try cock
C. increased amounts of sludge
D. fluctuation in the gauge glass

_____ **12.** Water is ___ to reduce the amount of dissolved oxygen.
A. heated
B. cooled
C. pressurized to 15 psi
D. all of the above

_____ **13.** Increased surface tension of boiler water can be caused by ___.
A. fuel oil inside the boiler
B. superheated steam
C. excessive pressure in the safety valve
D. water in the condensate

_____ **14.** Fuel oil is removed from the steam and water side of a boiler by using ___.
     A. sulfuric acid
     B. sulfate
     C. silica gel
     D. caustic soda

_____ **15.** ___ can lead to water hammer.
     A. Priming
     B. Carryover
     C. High surface tension
     D. all of the above

_____ **16.** Nonadhering sludge is removed from the boiler by using the ___.
     A. bottom try cock
     B. gauge glass blowdown valve
     C. bottom blowdown valve
     D. surface blowdown valve

_____ **17.** Hard water contains ___.
     A. scale-forming salts
     B. makeup chemicals
     C. oxygen scavengers
     D. sodium sulfite

Sludge Removal

_____ **1.** To blowdown line

_____ **2.** NOWL

_____ **3.** Bottom blowdown valve

_____ **4.** Boiler water circulation reduced

_____ **5.** Sludge

Priming and Carryover

_____ **1.** Boiling water

_____ **2.** Water carried into steam lines

_____ **3.** Feedwater

_____ **4.** High water level

_____ **5.** Boiler

Foaming

_____ **1.** Trapped steam bubbles

_____ **2.** Boiler

_____ **3.** Boiler water

_____ **4.** Film from impurities

_____ **5.** Steam bubbles

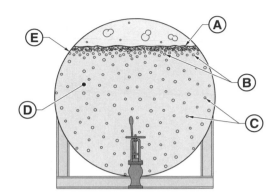

Water Treatment Log Readings

_____ **1.** Third day of month – condensate pH

_____ **2.** Sixth day of month – sodium sulfite present

_____ **3.** Second day of month – condensate TDS

_____ **4.** Fifth day of month – condensate hardness

_____ **5.** Fourth day of month – boiler water TDS

Heating and Chilling Plant
January
Boiler #1

Date	Boiler Water					Feedwater	Condensate			Products				Blowdown
	P	M	OH	TDS	Na_2SO_3	TDS	pH	TDS	Hard	938	8570	960	9980	
Max			400	3500	60		10.8							
Min			200	2500	30		10.0							
1	320	384	256	2700	45	45	10.8	15	0	44	4	4	12	3 / 1 hr
2	376	440	312	2900	60	39	10.8	16	0	32	8	0	0	3 / 2 hr
3	348	400	296	3000	55	36	10.9	16	0	32	6	0	8	3
4	324	380	268	2700	40	39	10.5	14	0	32	6	4	4	3
5	340	392	288	2900	45	34	10.7	14	0	32	6	4	8	3
6	272	328	216	2300	45	36	10.6	13	0	32	8	4	8	—
7	290	364	228	2600	35	34	10.8	13	0	36	4	4	8	—
8	311	396	336	2700	50	39	10.5	13	0	40	8	0	4	3

Bypass Feeder

_____ **1.** Bypass feeder tank

_____ **2.** Feedwater pump

_____ **3.** Stop valve

_____ **4.** Water treatment chemicals added

_____ **5.** Check valve

_____ **6.** Boiler

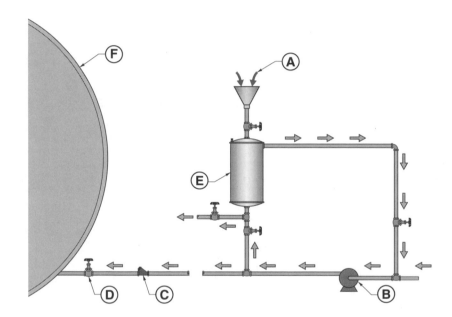

Additional Activities

1. Review Chapter 7 of *Low Pressure Boilers.*

2. Take the Quick Quiz® for Chapter 7 on the *Low Pressure Boilers* Interactive CD-ROM.

3. Review the following related Media Clips on the *Low Pressure Boilers* Interactive CD-ROM:
   • Boiler Scale
   • Bottom Blowdown
   • Caustic Embrittlement
   • High Water
   • pH

4. Review the Flash Cards for Chapter 7 on the *Low Pressure Boilers* Interactive CD-ROM.

Name _____ Date _____

True-False

T	F	**1.**	When taking over a shift, preliminary safety checks allow the boiler operator to identify any possible problems.
T	F	**2.**	A shift log helps the operator to complete all assigned tasks.
T	F	**3.**	In general, boilers should be blown down every 24 hr.
T	F	**4.**	The main steam stop valve should be closed during normal plant start-up.
T	F	**5.**	The boiler vent must be closed during warm-up to prevent pressure from escaping.
T	F	**6.**	The water level should be higher that the NOWL during bottom blowdown.
T	F	**7.**	The furnace brickwork should be cooled rapidly for energy efficiency.
T	F	**8.**	A boiler should be dumped when hot to allow the heat to be recovered.
T	F	**9.**	The boiler should be blown down when it is on a heavy load.
T	F	**10.**	The operator's hand should always be kept on the blowdown valve during blowdown.
T	F	**11.**	The blowdown valve should be kept open long enough for the water level in the gauge glass to drop out of sight.
T	F	**12.**	The quick-opening valve is opened first and closed last during blowdown.
T	F	**13.**	The low water fuel cutoff is checked for proper operation with the burner firing.
T	F	**14.**	Try cocks can be used as a boiler water level indicator.
T	F	**15.**	Steam discharged from the bottom try cock indicates a high water level.
T	F	**16.**	An evaporation test is performed by blowing down the low water fuel cutoff.
T	F	**17.**	Water added to a boiler with a low water level condition could cause a boiler explosion.
T	F	**18.**	Furnace explosions are caused by steam in the fuel oil.

ASME CODE SYMBOL STAMP	Before 2013	2013 and After	
	L	ASME L	**LOCOMOTIVE BOILER**

T   F   **19.** Any abnormal odor of gas should alert the boiler operator to a possible leak.

T   F   **20.** The boiler must be filled with water heated to 50°F before it is started for the first time.

T   F   **21.** Bottom blowdown is performed by opening the gauge glass blowdown valve.

T   F   **22.** Leaking fuel oil in the furnace could lead to a furnace explosion.

T   F   **23.** The boiler should be inspected to determine the cause of a low water level condition.

T   F   **24.** The furnace should not be purged after a flame failure.

T   F   **25.** A boiler must be taken off-line before it can be inspected.

T   F   **26.** Main steam stop valves must be locked out and tagged during a boiler inspection.

T   F   **27.** After a boiler is dumped, it should dry completely before cleaning.

T   F   **28.** A hydrostatic test is a steam test used to check for boiler leaks.

T   F   **29.** A malfunctioning steam trap can result in a steambound feedwater pump.

T   F   **30.** Tools and equipment must be provided for the boiler inspector during boiler inspection.

T   F   **31.** During a hydrostatic test, the boiler is half filled with water.

T   F   **32.** Dry lay-up is recommended for boilers that will be out of service for an extended period.

T   F   **33.** Moisture left on metal surfaces during dry lay-up could cause scale buildup.

T   F   **34.** More pounds of silica gel than quicklime are required when laying up a boiler dry.

T   F   **35.** All valves are opened during dry lay-up.

T   F   **36.** A scratch on the inside of a gauge glass can cause it to break.

T   F   **37.** A clean gauge glass is necessary to accurately determine boiler water level.

T   F   **38.** A boiler inspection is commonly performed by the plant manager.

T   F   **39.** An evaporation test lowers the boiler water level rapidly.

T   F   **40.** A steambound pump is caused by high water temperature.

T   F   **41.** All plants maintain boiler room logs for an 8-hour period.

T   F   **42.** A boiler room log can be used to determine the cause of a boiler shutdown.

T   F   **43.** Boiler lay-up is required when the boiler is out of service between shifts.

T   F   **44.** When warming up the boiler, the low water fuel cutoff should be blown down before the steam pressure gauge records pressure.

T   F   **45.** When shutting down the boiler, the main steam valve should be closed immediately after the furnace is shut down.

Multiple Choice

_____ **1.** The first thing a boiler operator should do when taking over a shift is ___.
- A. read the boiler room log
- B. check the fuel supply
- C. blow down the flash tank
- D. check the boiler water level

_____ **2.** When the low water fuel cutoff is blown down, ___.
- A. the water in the gauge glass will rise
- B. foaming is increased
- C. the burner should shut off
- D. none of the above

_____ **3.** The boiler pressure should always be ___ the header pressure when cutting a boiler in on the line.
- A. slightly above
- B. slightly below
- C. the same as
- D. none of the above

_____ **4.** The boiler should be blown down when it is ___.
- A. in high fire
- B. shut down
- C. on a light load
- D. all of the above

_____ **5.** ASME code states that on boilers having two bottom blowdown valves, the ___ valve should be closest to the boiler.
- A. screw
- B. quick-opening
- C. os&y
- D. globe

_____ **6.** After blowing down the water column and gauge glass, the water should ___ the gauge glass.
- A. flash to steam as it enters
- B. quickly enter
- C. slowly enter
- D. not enter

_____ **7.** If water cannot be seen in the gauge glass, ___.
- A. add water immediately
- B. the boiler inspector should be notified
- C. the fusible plug must be inspected
- D. the burner should be secured

_____ **8.** A furnace explosion can be caused by ___.
     A. a buildup of combustible gases or vapors
     B. leaking gas or fuel oil
     C. improper furnace purge
     D. all of the above

_____ **9.** The ___ blowdown valve is used to dump the boiler.
     A. bottom
     B. surface
     C. water column
     D. all of the above

_____ **10.** A method for checking for leaks in gas lines is ___.
     A. purging the furnace
     B. lighting a match
     C. applying soapy water
     D. none of the above

_____ **11.** A(n) ___ test is used to check for leaks in the boiler.
     A. evaporation
     B. low water
     C. caustic
     D. hydrostatic

_____ **12.** All traces of coal, soot, and ash must be removed to prevent ___ from forming when mixed with water.
     A. sodium sulfite
     B. zeolite
     C. sulfuric acid
     D. silica gel

_____ **13.** A steambound pump is caused by ___.
     A. excessive water temperature
     B. improper feedwater treatment
     C. low furnace temperature
     D. none of the above

_____ **14.** A(n) ___ test is used to test the low water fuel cutoff.
     A. hydrostatic
     B. evaporation
     C. dry lay-up
     D. vacuum

_____ **15.** A ___ is used to record information regarding operation of the boiler during a given period of time.
     A. chief instruction handbook
     B. pressure control
     C. pressure gauge
     D. boiler room log

_____ **16.** The boiler must be ___ when the low water fuel cutoff is blown down.
    A. shut down
    B. dumped
    C. firing
    D. in battery

_____ **17.** When the flame scanner is removed with the burner firing, the ___.
    A. fuel valve should open
    B. programmer should start the firing cycle
    C. burner should shut off
    D. all of the above

_____ **18.** To prevent damage to the furnace brickwork, the furnace ___.
    A. should be cooled slowly
    B. is lit off in high fire
    C. is purged before shutdown
    D. none of the above

_____ **19.** Boiler ___ is a condition when a boiler is operating at or above its maximum allowable working pressure.
    A. NOWL
    B. MAWP
    C. overpressure
    D. superheating

_____ **20.** Before dumping the boiler, the boiler heating surface should be ___.
    A. in high fire
    B. cool enough to touch
    C. higher than 337°F
    D. in low fire

_____ **21.** The water column whistle valve is ___ during the hydrostatic test.
    A. removed
    B. activated once
    C. sounded
    D. none of the above

_____ **22.** During the hydrostatic test, pressure on the boiler is brought up to ___ times the MAWP.
    A. 1½
    B. 2
    C. 2½
    D. 5

_____ **23.** Water used to fill the boiler during the hydrostatic test should be a minimum of ___°F.
    A. 0
    B. 12
    C. 32
    D. 70

_____ **24.** ___ can be placed on the water side of the boiler when placing the boiler in dry lay-up.
    A. Anthracite
    B. Quicklime
    C. Sulfite
    D. none of the above

_____ **25.** Gauge glass nuts are tightened by hand and then turned ___ with a wrench.
    A. ¾ of a turn
    B. 1½ turns
    C. 2 turns
    D. none of the above

_____ **26.** A ___ test is the most accurate method of testing the low water fuel cutoff.
    A. surface blowdown
    B. hydrostatic
    C. vacuum
    D. none of the above

_____ **27.** When testing a low water fuel cutoff, the burner should shut off when ___.
    A. water is still visible in the gauge glass
    B. the gauge glass is empty
    C. the float is removed
    D. all of the above

_____ **28.** The internal mechanism of a low water fuel cutoff should be periodically removed from the bowl to check and ___ the float ball.
    A. clean
    B. polish
    C. scale
    D. all of the above

_____ **29.** To correct a high water condition, a ___ is performed.
    A. low water fuel cutoff test
    B. surface blowdown
    C. bottom blowdown
    D. boiler vent test

_____ **30.** New ___ should be used when replacing a broken gauge glass.
    A. packing nuts
    B. glands
    C. seats
    D. washers

_____ **31.** A boiler is given a bottom blowdown to ___.
      A. discharge sludge
      B. control low water
      C. increase chemical concentrations
      D. all of the above

_____ **32.** A leak on gas lines and equipment must be repaired ___.
      A. by authorized personnel
      B. after the shift by the boiler operator
      C. only if the load is interrupted
      D. while the burner is still firing

_____ **33.** For maximum safety in operation of a low pressure boiler, the low water fuel cutoff should be tested ___.
      A. daily
      B. weekly
      C. monthly
      D. annually

_____ **34.** Boiler data that is commonly recorded on a boiler room log includes ___.
      A. boilers on line
      B. steam pressure
      C. condensate return temperature
      D. all of the above

_____ **35.** All running accessories (fuel oil pumps, fan, water pump, and burner) should be checked for proper ___.
      A. temperature
      B. pressure
      C. lubrication
      D. all of the above

_____ **36.** The proper testing of boiler accessories is determined by procedures suggested by ___.
      A. MAWP
      B. ABMA regulations
      C. ASME Code
      D. all of the above

_____ **37.** After testing the flame scanner, ___.
      A. the burner should go to high fire
      B. reset the programmer
      C. blow down the fuel oil return
      D. remove the burner tip

_____ **38.** During the evaporation test, the ___ is secured.
      A. fuel to the burner
      B. automatic city water makeup feeder
      C. gauge glass inlet
      D. all of the above

_____ **39.** During a boiler inspection, the main steam stop valve is ___.
      A. opened and tagged out
      B. closed, locked out, and tagged out
      C. opened partially to allow steam flow
      D. none of the above

_____ **40.** The ___ must be covered with water before water can be added safely.
      A. heating surface
      B. top try cock
      C. fuel oil valve
      D. vaporstat

Additional Activities

1. Review Chapter 8 of _Low Pressure Boilers._

2. Take the Quick Quiz® for Chapter 8 on the _Low Pressure Boilers_ Interactive CD-ROM.

3. Review the following related Media Clips on the _Low Pressure Boilers_ Interactive CD-ROM:
   • Boiler Room Log
   • Bottom Blowdown
   • Gauge Glass
   • Gauge Glass Blowdown
   • Gauge Glass Replacement
   • Flame Scanners
   • High Water
   • Low Water
   • Low Water Fuel Cutoff
   • Safety Valves
   • Water Column

4. Review the Flash Cards for Chapter 8 on the _Low Pressure Boilers_ Interactive CD-ROM.

Name _____ **Date** _____

True-False

T   F   **1.** Hot water heating systems produce heat more consistently than steam heating systems.

T   F   **2.** Hot water heating systems require less water to transfer the same amount of heat than steam heating systems.

T   F   **3.** The natural circulation hot water heating system uses circulating pumps to transport water in the system.

T   F   **4.** Water becomes less dense as it is heated.

T   F   **5.** The natural circulation hot water heating system uses a compression tank to absorb pressure changes.

T   F   **6.** Natural circulation hot water heating systems are commonly used in large contemporary buildings.

T   F   **7.** Floor-mounted circulating pumps are used in small plants.

T   F   **8.** Line-mounted circulating pumps operate intermittently, depending on plant requirements.

T   F   **9.** The forced circulation hot water heating system is vented to the atmosphere.

T   F   **10.** The aquastat controls the starting and stopping of the burner on a hot water boiler.

T   F   **11.** The flow control valve prevents natural circulation when water is not pumped in the forced circulation hot water system.

T   F   **12.** The pressure-reducing valve is used to prevent overpressure of water supplied to the expansion tank.

T   F   **13.** Diverter fittings are used to vent air from the heating units.

T   F   **14.** Stop valves before and after the pressure-reducing valve allow servicing of the pressure-reducing valve.

ASME CODE SYMBOL STAMP	Before 2013	2013 and After	WATER HEATER
		HLW	

T   F   **15.** The three-way mixing valve blends water returning from the heating units with supply water from the boiler.

T   F   **16.** All boilers are manufactured in conformance with Section I or IV of the ASME Boiler and Pressure Vessel Code.

T   F   **17.** An aquastat controls the burner by sensing steam pressure in a hot water boiler.

T   F   **18.** The strainer in the pressure-reducing valve should be inspected periodically for foreign matter.

T   F   **19.** The compression tank is normally full of water to feed into the boiler during a low water condition.

T   F   **20.** The relief valve should be located on the highest part of the boiler.

T   F   **21.** Relief valves should be manually tested every 30 days as recommended by the ASME Code.

T   F   **22.** Relief valves should discharge into the return line feeding into the circulating pump.

T   F   **23.** A temperature-pressure gauge has two scales.

T   F   **24.** Hydrostatic pressure is expressed in pounds per square inch (psi).

T   F   **25.** Air controls are used to allow water to drain from the compression tank.

T   F   **26.** Air removed from the boiler water is diverted to the compression tank in a forced circulation hot water heating system.

T   F   **27.** An aquastat commonly has a temperature differential preset by the manufacturer.

T   F   **28.** The aquastat temperature differential setting controls the starting and stopping of the circulating pump.

T   F   **29.** Two diverter fittings may be required for heating units above the supply line where resistance to circulation is high.

T   F   **30.** Hot water heating systems require special hot water boiler accessories.

Multiple Choice

_____   **1.** A typical steam heating system operates at temperatures above ___°F.
         A. 150
         B. 170
         C. 212
         D. 300

_____   **2.** A hot water heating system operates at ___ the steam heating system.
         A. a higher temperature than
         B. a lower temperature than
         C. the same temperature as
         D. all of the above

_____ **3.** In a natural circulation hot water heating system, the ___ functions as a relief valve.
 A. supply line
 B. return line
 C. heating unit
 D. expansion tank

_____ **4.** ___ pressure is water pressure per vertical foot exerted at the base of a column of water.
 A. Normal operating water
 B. Electrostatic
 C. Hydrostatic
 D. none of the above

_____ **5.** In a remote temperature-monitoring system, the burner is controlled based on ___.
 A. steam pressure
 B. temperature of air at the heating unit
 C. outside air temperature
 D. makeup water

_____ **6.** Steam boilers are classified as "high pressure" if steam pressure exceeds ___ psi.
 A. 7
 B. 15
 C. 20
 D. 160

_____ **7.** A flow control valve functions similarly to a(n) ___ valve to prevent natural water circulation.
 A. air separator
 B. pressure reducing
 C. check
 D. gate

_____ **8.** Hot water boilers operating with a 250°F water temperature and ___ psi water pressure or less are classified as low pressure.
 A. 10
 B. 15
 C. 100
 D. 160

_____ **9.** Hot water boilers can be ___ boilers.
 A. firetube
 B. watertube
 C. cast iron sectional
 D. all of the above

_____ **10.** A hot water boiler relief valve is rated in ___ relieved per hour.
 A. Btu
 B. pounds of water pressure
 C. pounds of water temperature
 D. none of the above

_____ **11.** A steam boiler safety valve is rated in ___ relieved per hour.
    A. Btu
    B. pounds of steam
    C. Btu of water temperature
    D. all of the above

_____ **12.** A relief valve must be built according to the ___.
    A. ASME Code
    B. ABMA Code
    C. boiler manufacturer specifications
    D. none of the above

_____ **13.** The relieving pressure of a relief valve on a low pressure hot water boiler cannot exceed ___ psi.
    A. 15
    B. 30
    C. 160
    D. 250

_____ **14.** The two types of low water fuel cutoffs normally used on hot water boilers are the ___-type and the probe-type cutoffs.
    A. electrostatic
    B. electronic
    C. float
    D. flow

_____ **15.** The ___ tank is normally half full of water to maintain the correct water level in the forced circulation hot water heating system.
    A. expansion
    B. compression
    C. receiver
    D. vacuum

_____ **16.** Section VI of the ASME Code recommends relief valves be manually tested ___.
    A. once a shift
    B. every 24 hours
    C. every 30 days
    D. none of the above

_____ **17.** The ___ protects the hot water heating system from exceeding the MAWP.
    A. aquastat
    B. blowdown valve
    C. relief valve
    D. compression tank

_____ **18.** The ___ controls the starting and stopping of the burner by sensing the temperature in the hot water boiler.
    A. flow control valve
    B. diverter fitting
    C. circulating pump
    D. aquastat

_____ **19.** The temperature-pressure gauge indicates the temperature and pressure of the water ___.
  A. in the heating unit
  B. leaving the boiler
  C. in the compression tank
  D. at the mixing valve

_____ **20.** ___ direct the flow of hot water supplied to and returned from the heating units.
  A. Flow control valves
  B. Hand-operated valves
  C. Steam traps
  D. Diverter fittings

_____ **21.** A ___ prevents natural circulation when hot water is not being pumped through the forced circulation hot water system.
  A. stop valve
  B. diverter fitting
  C. circulating pump
  D. flow control valve

_____ **22.** A pressure-reducing valve reduces the pressure of city water to approximately ___ psi.
  A. 4 to 6
  B. 8 to 10
  C. 10 to 15
  D. 12 to 18

_____ **23.** A(n) ___ allows bleeding of trapped air in a heating unit.
  A. steam trap
  B. diverter fitting
  C. air vent
  D. air control

_____ **24.** If the compression tank is allowed to fill with water, pressure will increase, causing the ___.
  A. pressure-reducing valve to activate
  B. relief valve to open
  C. air control to drain the water
  D. all of the above

_____ **25.** Some compression tanks are equipped with a ___ for determining the compression tank water level.
  A. sight glass
  B. try cock
  C. gauge glass
  D. none of the above

Natural Circulation Hot Water Heating System

_____ **1.** Vent line

_____ **2.** Heating unit

_____ **3.** Overflow line

_____ **4.** Boiler

_____ **5.** Expansion tank

_____ **6.** Branch line

_____ **7.** Return line

_____ **8.** Supply line

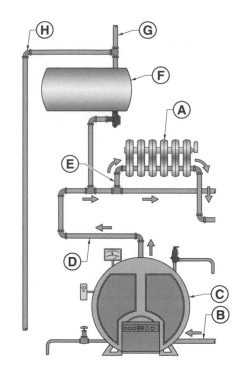

Aquastat

_____ **1.** Air separator

_____ **2.** Setpoint adjustor

_____ **3.** Thermostat

_____ **4.** Boiler

_____ **5.** Cover

_____ **6.** Remote bulb sensor

_____ **7.** Aquastat

_____ **8.** Burner controls

_____ **9.** Heating units

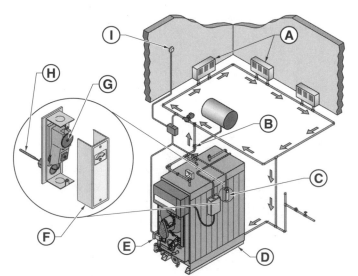

Forced Circulation Hot Water Heating System

_____ 1. Air separator

_____ 2. Heating unit

_____ 3. Temperature-pressure gauge

_____ 4. Drain

_____ 5. Compression tank

_____ 6. Backflow preventer

_____ 7. Boiler

_____ 8. Compression tank valve

_____ 9. Air vent

_____ 10. Aquastat

_____ 11. Bypass valve

_____ 12. Stop valve

_____ 13. Air control tank fitting

_____ 14. Flow control valve

_____ 15. Makeup water supply line

_____ 16. Pressure-reducing valve

_____ 17. Diverter fitting

_____ 18. Relief valve

_____ 19. Bypass line

_____ 20. Circulating pump

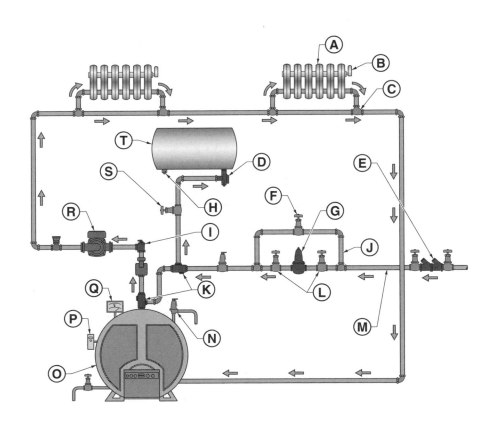

Relief Valve

_____ 1. Sealing diaphragm

_____ 2. Body

_____ 3. Outlet

_____ 4. Spring

_____ 5. Data plate

_____ 6. Try lever

_____ 7. Inlet

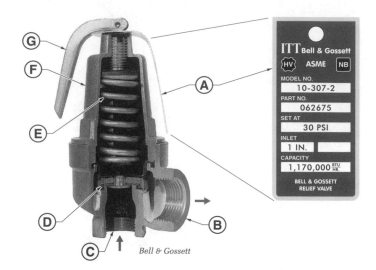

Bell & Gossett

Additional Activities

1. Review Chapter 9 of _Low Pressure Boilers_.

2. Take the Quick Quiz® for Chapter 9 on the _Low Pressure Boilers_ Interactive CD-ROM.

3. Review the following related Media Clip on the _Low Pressure Boilers_ Interactive CD-ROM:
   • Centrifugal Pumps

4. Review the Flash Cards for Chapter 9 on the _Low Pressure Boilers_ Interactive CD-ROM.

Name _____ **Date** _____

True-False

T	F	**1.**	Water transports heat more efficiently than air.
T	F	**2.**	Some cooling systems can be designed to share components with a hot water heating system.
T	F	**3.**	Chiller systems are commonly used to cool building spaces and for refrigeration in food processing.
T	F	**4.**	Heat flows from a cold material to a hot material.
T	F	**5.**	A measurement of the quantity of heat transfer is the British thermal unit (Btu).
T	F	**6.**	Latent heat is the amount of heat that changes the temperature of a substance but not the state of a substance.
T	F	**7.**	When refrigerant gas is compressed, the temperature and pressure are lowered.
T	F	**8.**	Refrigerant is converted from a gas to a liquid in the condenser.
T	F	**9.**	An absorption refrigeration system uses a compressor to provide pressurized ammonia to the system.
T	F	**10.**	Refrigerant is changed from a liquid to a gas in the low pressure side of a compression system.
T	F	**11.**	Latent heat is heat added to a substance that changes its state without a change in temperature.
T	F	**12.**	In a compression refrigeration system, heat transfer occurs at the expansion valve and the compressor.
T	F	**13.**	When ice changes into water, there is a change in state.
T	F	**14.**	In a refrigeration system, heat is absorbed when a fluid changes from a liquid to a gas.
T	F	**15.**	A scroll compressor has reciprocating cylinders to compress the refrigerant.
T	F	**16.**	The evaporator is located on the high pressure side of a cooling system.
T	F	**17.**	A refrigerant absorbs heat when changing from a liquid to a gaseous state.

ASME CODE SYMBOL STAMP	**Before 2013**	**2013 and After**	**ELECTRIC BOILER**

T   F   **18.** Direct cooling systems are used where the space or product to be cooled is located a considerable distance from the condensing equipment.

T   F   **19.** Refrigerants used in a compression refrigeration system must have a boiling point below the temperature of the air to be cooled.

T   F   **20.** If the pressure on a refrigerant increases, the boiling point decreases.

T   F   **21.** In a direct cooling system, the evaporator is in direct contact with the space or product being cooled.

T   F   **22.** Compression refrigeration systems are commonly used for air conditioning applications.

T   F   **23.** Heat is released by the refrigerant at the evaporator.

T   F   **24.** Liquid refrigerant leaves the condenser under high pressure before reaching the expansion valve.

T   F   **25.** In cooling mode, an indoor coil is the condenser.

T   F   **26.** In an absorption system, heat is applied at the generator.

T   F   **27.** Indirect cooling systems use refrigerant piped to the space or product to be cooled.

T   F   **28.** Chlorofluorocarbons (CFCs) are present in all refrigerants used in compression systems.

T   F   **29.** Cooling systems use equipment similar to hot water heating systems.

T   F   **30.** Air conditioning systems are cooling systems used to cool air for comfort in building spaces.

Multiple Choice

_____ **1.** Water chilled in a cooling system is chilled by the ___.
    A. boiler
    B. chiller
    C. condenser
    D. compressor

_____ **2.** Heat added to a substance that changes its state without a change in temperature is ___ heat.
    A. super
    B. sensible
    C. latent
    D. mechanical

_____ **3.** In a(n) ___ system, water is commonly used to absorb heat from the product or space to be cooled.
    A. ammonia
    B. direct cooling
    C. direct-expansion
    D. chilled water

4. In a compression refrigeration system, liquid refrigerant under high pressure is allowed to drop in pressure by the ___.
  A. absorber
  B. absorbent
  C. expansion valve
  D. all of the above

_____ **5.** Absorption refrigeration systems may use ___ as a refrigerant.
  A. pure water
  B. R-134a and water
  C. pure R-134a
  D. lithium bromide and water

_____ **6.** Cooling units that cool building spaces are designed to ___ heat from the air.
  A. sense
  B. release
  C. condense
  D. absorb

_____ **7.** In a refrigeration system, heat is ___ when a fluid changes from a gas to a liquid.
  A. decreased
  B. absorbed
  C. released
  D. compressed

_____ **8.** In a compression refrigeration system, high pressure vapor is converted from a gas to a liquid in the ___.
  A. evaporator
  B. compressor
  C. generator
  D. condenser

_____ **9.** In a compression refrigeration system, the refrigerant absorbs heat in the ___.
  A. evaporator
  B. compressor
  C. generator
  D. none of the above

_____ **10.** In a lithium bromide and water refrigeration system, heat is commonly applied with steam coil at the ___.
  A. evaporator
  B. compressor
  C. generator
  D. condenser

_____ **11.** In a lithium bromide system, cooling water is directed through the ___ and condenser to remove heat.
  A. evaporator
  B. absorber
  C. generator
  D. all of the above

_____ **12.** Indirect cooling systems commonly use ___ as a medium to cool the space or product.
    A. CFCs
    B. chilled water
    C. lithium bromide
    D. freon

_____ **13.** In a compression refrigeration system, heat is absorbed by the refrigerant in the ___.
    A. low pressure side
    B. high pressure side
    C. condenser coils
    D. generator

_____ **14.** Common condenser designs include ___ condensers.
    A. shell-and-coil
    B. shell-and-tube
    C. tube-in-tube
    D. all of the above

_____ **15.** In a compression refrigeration system, the ___ is used to change the pressure of a refrigerant gas.
    A. compressor
    B. absorber
    C. condenser
    D. steam coil

_____ **16.** The compressor will be damaged if ___ refrigerant is allowed to enter.
    A. gaseous
    B. liquid
    C. CFC
    D. all of the above

_____ **17.** Refrigerants used in a compression system must be ___.
    A. toxic
    B. chemically reactive
    C. flammable
    D. nonflammable

_____ **18.** An absorption refrigeration system includes all of the following except the ___.
    A. condenser
    B. compressor
    C. evaporator
    D. generator

_____ **19.** ___ refrigerants do not contain chlorine and are safer for the enviornment.
    A. HCFC
    B. CFC
    C. HFC
    D. all of the above

_____ **20.** In indirect cooling systems, ___ used as a medium must be kept above 32°F.
   A. ammonia
   B. lithium
   C. water
   D. freon

Refrigeration Cycle

_____ **1.** Cool air

_____ **2.** Hot air

_____ **3.** Metering device

_____ **4.** Evaporator

_____ **5.** Compressor

_____ **6.** Condenser

Centrifugal Compressor

_____ **1.** Drive shaft

_____ **2.** Housing

_____ **3.** Impeller wheel

_____ **4.** Inlet port

_____ **5.** Outlet port

Ammonia-Water Absorption Chiller System

_____ **1.** Generator

_____ **2.** Expansion valve

_____ **3.** Evaporator

_____ **4.** Regulating valve

_____ **5.** Absorber

_____ **6.** Condenser

_____ **7.** Pump

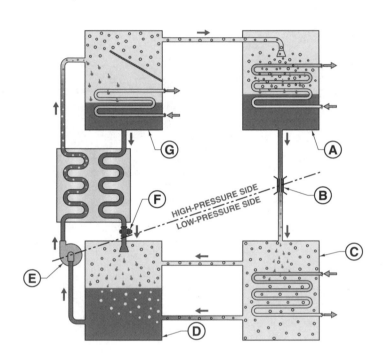

Cooling System Application – Pasteurization Process

_____ **1.** Cooled milk

_____ **2.** Warm water out

_____ **3.** Collection trough

_____ **4.** Heated milk enters cooler

_____ **5.** Milk passing around piping

_____ **6.** Chilled water in

_____ **7.** Piping containing chilled water

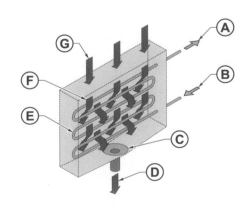

Chilled Water System

_____ **1.** Compressor

_____ **2.** Metering device

_____ **3.** Cooling tower

_____ **4.** Air duct

_____ **5.** Evaporator

_____ **6.** Ceiling

_____ **7.** Condenser

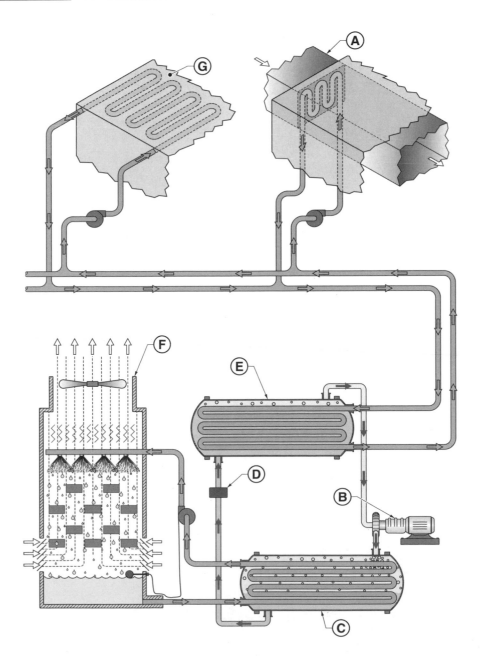

Additional Activities

1. Review Chapter 10 of *Low Pressure Boilers*.

2. Take the Quick Quiz® for Chapter 10 on the *Low Pressure Boilers* Interactive CD-ROM.

3. Review the following related Media Clips on the *Low Pressure Boilers* Interactive CD-ROM:
   • Indirect Cooling Systems
   • Heating/Cooling Coils

4. Review the Flash Cards for Chapter 10 on the *Low Pressure Boilers* Interactive CD-ROM.

Name _____ **Date** _____

True-False

T F **1.** An accident can occur at any time.

T F **2.** All accidents should be reported regardless of the nature of the injury.

T F **3.** Accident report forms are filed in the boiler room log.

T F **4.** Combustible materials require special safety procedures when handling.

T F **5.** Local fire departments are responsible for maintaining a safe boiler room.

T F **6.** OSHA standards are reproduced in the Code of Federal Regulations (CFR).

T F **7.** The NFPA is a federal agency established to control and abate pollution.

T F **8.** Fire extinguishers are identified by the type of fire that the extinguisher is designed to be used on.

T F **9.** Eye protection is required when visually inspecting the furnace fire.

T F **10.** An insurance agency may require special trim and accessories for maximum safety in a particular plant.

T F **11.** All unsafe conditions in the boiler room should be reported.

T F **12.** The ABMA is a government regulatory agency.

T F **13.** When testing safety valves, stand clear to avoid possible injury.

T F **14.** Horseplay in the boiler room is permissible away from the boiler furnace.

T F **15.** To save time, always run in the event of an emergency.

T F **16.** Spontaneous combustion can be caused by improper storage of oily rags.

ASME CODE SYMBOL STAMP	Before 2013	2013 and After	**UNFIRED PRESSURE VESSEL**

T F **17.** All facilities must have a fire safety plan.

T F **18.** A permit-required confined space requires a signed entry permit by the entry supervisor.

Multiple Choice

_____ **1.** Accident reports include ___.
  A. name of injured person
  B. date, time, and place of accident
  C. nature of duty
  D. all of the above

_____ **2.** A(n) ___ is printed material used to relay chemical hazard information from the manufacturer to the employer.
  A. OSHA CFR
  B. MSDS
  C. NFPA bulletin
  D. EPA certificate

_____ **3.** The ___ is responsible for the safe and efficient operation of the boiler.
  A. chief engineer
  B. fire brigade
  C. head custodian
  D. boiler operator

_____ **4.** When the boiler is removed from service, the first thing to do is ___.
  A. lockout and tag the steam stop valves
  B. coat the tubes with oil to prevent rusting
  C. drill drain holes to ensure removal of water
  D. all of the above

_____ **5.** The ___ uses a four-color diamond-shaped sign to display basic information about hazardous material.
  A. RTK label
  B. HMIG label
  C. NFPA Hazard Signal System
  D. none of the above

_____ **6.** ___ are used to store combustible liquids.
  A. Flash tanks
  B. Approved safety cans
  C. Vacuum pumps
  D. all of the above

_____ **7.** The ___ should be opened to prevent a vacuum in the boiler before opening a manhole.
    A. feedwater pump
    B. vacuum tank
    C. boiler vent
    D. blowdown

_____ **8.** ___ is required to start and sustain a fire.
    A. Heat
    B. Fuel
    C. Oxygen
    D. all of the above

_____ **9.** Boiler valves should be opened ___ to prevent water hammer.
    A. quickly
    B. slowly
    C. rapidly and often
    D. none of the above

_____ **10.** A ___ hazard on the NFPA Hazard Signal System is the likelihood of a material to cause injury due to acute exposure.
    A. special
    B. reactivity
    C. flammability
    D. health

_____ **11.** Ear protection devices are rated for noise reduction with a(n) ___ number.
    A. NRR
    B. EPA
    C. OSHA
    D. ASME

_____ **12.** A(n) ___ is required for protection against airborne contaminants when cleaning boiler refractory.
    A. hard hat
    B. ear protection device
    C. respirator
    D. none of the above

_____ **13.** The number and type of fire extinguishers needed are determined by ___.
    A. how fast the fire may spread
    B. potential heat intensity
    C. accessibility to fire
    D. all of the above

_____ **14.** When blowing down the boiler, the quick-opening valve should be ___.
    A. opened first and closed last
    B. opened after the screw valve
    C. opened first and closed first
    D. none of the above

_____ **15.** A lockout/tagout must be removed ___.
        A. by the worker who installed it
        B. by authorized personnel
        C. in accordance with written lockout/tagout procedures
        D. all of the above

_____ **16.** A(n) ___ is a person who is trained in, and has specific knowledge of, the construction and operation of electrical equipment or a specific task.
        A. electrician
        B. qualified person
        C. boiler operator
        D. stationary engineer

Hazardous Material Container Labeling – RTK Labeling

_____ **1.** Health hazards

_____ **2.** Signal word

_____ **3.** Chemical or common name

_____ **4.** Physical hazards

_____ **5.** Handling and storage instructions

_____ **6.** First aid procedures for exposure or contact

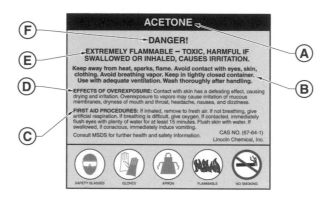

Additional Activities

1. Review Chapter 11 of _Low Pressure Boilers._

2. Take the Quick Quiz® for Chapter 11 on the _Low Pressure Boilers_ Interactive CD-ROM.

3. Review the following related Media Clips on the _Low Pressure Boilers_ Interactive CD-ROM:
    • Lockout
    • Lockout/Tagout Procedure
    • OSHA
    • Shower and Eye Wash

4. Review the Flash Cards for Chapter 11 on the _Low Pressure Boilers_ Interactive CD-ROM.

Name _____ **Date** _____

True-False

T   F   **1.** All steam boilers must have one or more safety valves.

T   F   **2.** A hydrostatic test determines whether a steam boiler has sufficient relieving capacity.

T   F   **3.** The main steam stop valve, bottom blowdown valves, and feedwater valves should be locked closed before anyone enters the boiler drum.

T   F   **4.** Scale protects the boiler heating surfaces.

T   F   **5.** Boiler corrosion cannot be prevented as long as water is in contact with metal.

T   F   **6.** Water begins to boil at approximately 212°F at atmospheric pressure.

T   F   **7.** Fuels most commonly used in boilers are fuel oil, gas, and coal.

T   F   **8.** Safety valves on steam boilers are designed to open slowly.

T   F   **9.** The steam pressure gauge must be connected to the highest part of the steam side of the boiler.

T   F   **10.** With an NOWL in a boiler, the gauge glass is approximately half full.

T   F   **11.** A high surface tension on top of the boiler water can lead to foaming.

Identify the ASME Code Symbol Stamps.

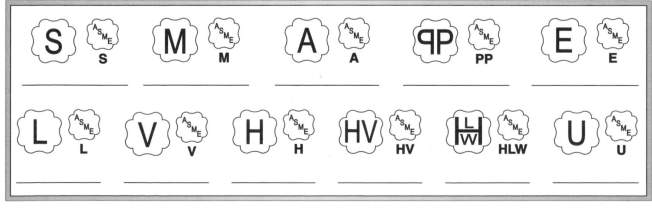

Multiple Choice

_____ **1.** The bottom blowdown on a boiler ___.
  A. removes sludge and sediment from the mud drum
  B. reduces boiler steam pressure
  C. adds makeup water to the boiler
  D. increases boiler priming

_____ **2.** A boiler fusible plug is brass or bronze with a core of ___.
  A. zinc
  B. tin
  C. titanium
  D. iron oxide

_____ **3.** A steam pressure gauge is calibrated in ___.
  A. pounds per cubic inch
  B. pounds per square inch
  C. inches of water column
  D. inches of water gauge

_____ **4.** Fires caused by spontaneous combustion are most likely to occur in the ___.
  A. fuel oil tank
  B. oily waste rag storage
  C. boiler furnace
  D. boiler ash pit

_____ **5.** The ___ are a secondary means of determining boiler water level.
  A. water columns
  B. gauge glass blowdown valves
  C. high and low water alarms
  D. try cocks

_____ **6.** A siphon installed between the boiler and the pressure gauge protects the Bourdon tube from ___ reaching the pressure gauge.
  A. water
  B. gases of combustion
  C. steam
  D. fuel

_____ **7.** Boiler feedwater is chemically treated to ___.
  A. increase circulation
  B. increase oxygen concentration
  C. prevent formation of scale
  D. increase boiler makeup water

_____ **8.** In a firetube boiler, soot accumulates on the ___.
      A. inside tube surface
      B. outside tube surface
      C. waterwall surface
      D. lowest part of the water side

_____ **9.** The pressure applied on the boiler during a hydrostatic test should be ___ times the MAWP.
      A. 1½
      B. 2
      C. 2½
      D. 3

_____ **10.** As fuel oil is heated, its viscosity is ___.
      A. the same
      B. increased
      C. decreased
      D. ignited

_____ **11.** The induced draft fan is located between the boiler and the ___.
      A. feedwater pump
      B. condensate return tank
      C. evaporator
      D. chimney

_____ **12.** The flash point of fuel oil is the minimum temperature at which the fuel will ___.
      A. support combustion
      B. no longer flow
      C. flash when exposed to an open flame
      D. have its highest Btu content

_____ **13.** The fire point of fuel oil is the minimum temperature at which the fuel oil will ___.
      A. burn continually
      B. no longer flash
      C. flash when exposed to an open flame
      D. have its highest Btu content

_____ **14.** The pour point of fuel oil is the ___ temperature at which fuel oil will ___.
      A. lowest; burn
      B. lowest; flow
      C. highest; burn
      D. highest; flow

_____ **15.** Fuel oil with a low flash point is ___.
          A. used with high pressure boilers
          B. dangerous to handle
          C. only used in low pressure plants
          D. heated to increase its viscosity

_____ **16.** The operating range of a steam boiler is controlled by a(n) ___.
          A. pressure control
          B. air flow interlock
          C. flame scanner
          D. programmer

_____ **17.** Water hammer in steam lines is caused by ___.
          A. low steam pressure
          B. high steam pressure
          C. condensate in the line
          D. a sudden drop in plant load

_____ **18.** A manometer measures ___.
          A. flue gas temperature
          B. volume of fuel oil flow
          C. atmospheric pressure
          D. difference in pressure between two points

_____ **19.** The best time to blow down a boiler is when it is ___.
          A. at its peak load
          B. at 75% of its peak load
          C. at its lowest load
          D. being taken out of service

_____ **20.** Boilers that are laid up dry have trays of ___ put in the steam and water drums to absorb moisture.
          A. calcium chloride
          B. hot soda lime
          C. silica gel
          D. potash

_____ **21.** To obtain complete combustion of a fuel, ___, ___, ___, and ___ are required.
          A. mixture; atomization; temperature; time
          B. CO_2; O_2; CO; CO_3
          C. turbulence; feedwater; air; flue gas
          D. hot refractory; air; draft; gases of combustion

_____ **22.** Oxygen in the boiler causes ___.
          A. scale
          B. pitting
          C. foaming
          D. carryover

_____ **23.** When the boiler low water alarm is ringing, the operator should ___.
      A. call the chief engineer
      B. increase the firing rate
      C. decrease the feedwater
      D. secure the fires and feedwater

_____ **24.** A furnace explosion can be prevented by ___.
      A. checking the water level once a shift
      B. testing the safety valves once a month
      C. purging the furnace after ignition failure
      D. testing the safety valve regularly

_____ **25.** A lead sulfide cell, which is used for flame detection, is sensitive to ___.
      A. infrared light
      B. visible light
      C. ultra violet light
      D. temperature increases

_____ **26.** A pop safety valve is a ___ type.
      A. hand and lever
      B. pin and disc
      C. deadweight
      D. spring-loaded

_____ **27.** To test a low water fuel cutoff using an evaporation test, the boiler operator must ___.
      A. close the condensate return valve
      B. secure all of the feedwater going to the boiler
      C. completely drain the regulator chamber
      D. have an inspector on hand

_____ **28.** The ___ Hazard Signal System provides container label information about hazardous material.
      A. ASME
      B. NFPA
      C. EPA
      D. ANSI

_____ **29.** To prevent a vacuum from forming on a boiler that is coming off-line, ___.
      A. open the boiler vent
      B. blow down the boiler
      C. dump the boiler
      D. pop the safety valve

_____ **30.** Low pressure boilers equipped with quick-opening and screw valves are blown down by opening the ___ valve first and closing it ___.
      A. quick-opening; first
      B. screw; last
      C. quick-opening; last
      D. quick-opening valves are never used on low pressure boilers

_____ **31.** The viscosity of fuel oil is the measurement of the ___ of the fuel oil.
A. Btu content
B. fire point
C. flash point
D. internal resistance to flow

_____ **32.** Feedwater is treated chemically before it enters the boiler to ___.
A. prevent foaming
B. eliminate blowing down the boiler
C. change the scale-forming salts to a sludge that will raise the boiler water temperature
D. change scale-forming salts to a nonadhering sludge

_____ **33.** Complete combustion is defined as burning all fuel using ___.
A. the theoretical amount of air
B. a minimal amount of excess air
C. no excess air
D. CO_2 and CO

_____ **34.** When testing the safety valve by hand, there should be at least ___ psi of pressure on the boiler.
A. 1
B. 5
C. 15
D. 160

_____ **35.** The water column on a low pressure steam boiler ___.
A. reduces fluctuation in water level to prevent carryover
B. reduces the turbulence of water in the gauge glass
C. provides a place to install the bottom blowdown valve
D. a water column is never used on a low pressure boiler

_____ **36.** Safety valves on low pressure boilers can be tested ___.
A. only by hand
B. only by pressure
C. by hand or by pressure
D. safety valves should never be tested

_____ **37.** Before laying up a boiler, the boiler operator must ___.
A. notify the boiler inspector
B. remove the boiler certificate
C. thoroughly clean the fire and water sides
D. only clean the water side because soot acts as an insulator

_____ **38.** If water comes out of the top try cock, the boiler operator must ___.
A. notify the engineer
B. blow down the boiler
C. bypass the try cocks and feed by hand
D. leave the boiler alone, this is normal

_____ **39.** If steam comes out of the bottom try cock, the boiler operator must ___.
      A. secure the fires and feedwater to the boiler, allow the boiler to cool slowly, and notify the boiler inspector
      B. bypass the try cocks and feed by hand
      C. leave the boiler alone, this is normal
      D. start up a new feedwater pump

_____ **40.** A scotch marine boiler is a ___ boiler.
      A. watertube
      B. cast iron
      C. cast iron firetube
      D. firetube

_____ **41.** When performing a hydrostatic test on a boiler, ___.
      A. all safety valves are removed or gagged
      B. the boiler vent is closed
      C. the main steam stop valve is closed
      D. all of the above

_____ **42.** ___ is the difference in pressure between two points of measurement that causes air or gases to flow.
      A. Draft
      B. Feedwater
      C. Condensate
      D. Carryover

_____ **43.** No. 6 fuel oil has ___ viscosity when compared to No. 2 fuel oil.
      A. no
      B. high
      C. medium
      D. low

_____ **44.** ___ is heat transfer that occurs when molecules in a material are heated and the heat is passed from molecule to molecule through the material.
      A. Combustion
      B. Conduction
      C. Condensation
      D. none of the above

_____ **45.** Confined space is ___.
      A. large enough for an employee to enter
      B. not designed for continuous employee access
      C. restricted in means for entry and exit
      D. all of the above

Name _____ Date _____

True-False

T F **1.** To prevent water hammer, water should be removed from all steam lines.

T F **2.** Pressure on water does not change the boiling point of the water.

T F **3.** A Bourdon tube in a steam pressure gauge is filled with live steam when it is operating.

T F **4.** A steam trap is a device that removes air and condensate without loss of steam.

T F **5.** Treated water is used in a boiler to prevent pitting of the boiler metal.

T F **6.** When dumping a boiler, there should be at least 2 lb of steam in the boiler to force water from the boiler.

T F **7.** The boiler vent should be open when filling the boiler with water.

T F **8.** The pressure control must be mounted in a vertical position to ensure accurate operation.

T F **9.** A burner should always start up in high fire to ensure enough fuel for ignition.

T F **10.** Carrying too high a water level in the boiler could lead to water hammer.

Multiple Choice

_____ **1.** On boilers that have both quick-opening and screw blowdown valves, the quick-opening valve must be located ___.
   A. after the screw valve
   B. at the NOWL
   C. closest to the boiler and followed by the screw valve
   D. on the boiler vent line

_____ **2.** Entering a boiler for maintenance may require a(n) ___.
   A. OSHA certification
   B. ASME license
   C. boiler operator license
   D. confined space permit

_____ **3.** The Bourdon tube in a steam pressure gauge is protected by a ___.
    A. steam trap
    B. siphon
    C. steam strainer
    D. stopcock

_____ **4.** Draft is measured with a ___.
    A. pyrometer
    B. hydrometer
    C. manometer
    D. thermocouple

_____ **5.** A steam boiler is blown down to ___.
    A. lower the oxygen level
    B. test the safety valve
    C. remove sludge and sediment
    D. clean the feedwater lines

_____ **6.** The NOWL in a steam boiler is indicated when ___.
    A. steam and water flow out of the middle try cock
    B. water flows out of the top try cock
    C. steam flows out of the bottom try cock
    D. steam and water flow out of the top try cock

_____ **7.** A compound gauge indicates ___.
    A. differential pressure
    B. pressure or vacuum
    C. absolute pressure
    D. the sum of the pressure on two boilers

_____ **8.** Atomization of fuel oil in a rotary cup burner is caused by the ___.
    A. rotating cup and secondary air
    B. rotating cup and primary air
    C. pressure of the fuel oil
    D. secondary and primary air

_____ **9.** The try cocks on a water column are used ___.
    A. as a secondary means of determining the water level
    B. to blow down the water column
    C. for testing the flame scanner
    D. to remove impurities from the surface of the water

_____ **10.** A low pressure steam boiler has a maximum allowable working pressure (MAWP) of up to ___ psi.
    A. 15
    B. 35
    C. 100
    D. low pressure boilers have no MAWP

_____ **11.** In a firetube boiler, the heat and gases of combustion pass ___.
        A. through the tubes
        B. around the tubes
        C. only through the combustion chamber
        D. both A and B

_____ **12.** Safety valve connections must be made according to the requirements of the ___.
        A. fire department
        B. shift foreman
        C. American Society of Mechanical Engineers (ASME)
        D. American Boiler Manufacturers Association (ABMA)

_____ **13.** Boiler fittings are necessary for ___.
        A. safety
        B. efficiency
        C. cosmetic purposes
        D. both A and B

_____ **14.** The most important fitting on a boiler is the ___.
        A. low water fuel cutoff
        B. feedwater regulator
        C. superheater
        D. safety valve

_____ **15.** A safety valve ___.
        A. controls the boiler operating range
        B. controls high or low water
        C. prevents the boiler from exceeding its MAWP
        D. controls high and low fire

_____ **16.** Safety valves are designed to ___.
        A. open slowly to prevent water hammer
        B. pop open
        C. open only by hand
        D. open slowly and then close with no drop in pressure

_____ **17.** A steam pressure gauge is calibrated in ___.
        A. pounds per cubic inch
        B. inches of water column
        C. pounds per temperature increase
        D. pounds per square inch

_____ **18.** Bottom blowdown lines on a watertube boiler are located on the ___.
        A. feedwater pump
        B. bottom of the mud drum
        C. fuel oil pump inlet
        D. lowest part of the combustion chamber

_____ **19.** When blowing down a boiler equipped with a quick-opening valve and a screw valve, the quick-opening valve is ___.

    A. opened first and closed last

    B. opened last and closed first

    C. opened first and closed first

    D. opened as operator prefers

_____ **20.** If a quick-opening valve is used as a bottom blowdown valve, it must be located ___.

    A. between the boiler and the screw valve

    B. furthest from the shell of the boiler

    C. cannot be used on low pressure boilers

    D. none of the above

_____ **21.** Surface tension on the water in the steam and water drum is increased by ___.

    A. impurities that float on the surface of the water

    B. inexperienced boiler operators

    C. very soft water

    D. a high steam load

_____ **22.** The surface blowdown line on a boiler is located at the ___.

    A. MAWP

    B. NOWL

    C. lowest heating surface

    D. bottom try cock

_____ **23.** Draft is defined as a difference in pressure that causes ___.

    A. air or gases to flow

    B. a balance of pressure

    C. a back pressure

    D. none of the above

_____ **24.** Natural draft is produced by a(n) ___.

    A. forced draft fan

    B. induced draft fan (used in larger plants)

    C. difference in temperature of a column of gas inside the chimney from a column of air outside the chimney

    D. clean coal bed

_____ **25.** A draft fan located between the boiler and chimney is used in a(n) ___ draft system.

    A. natural

    B. forced

    C. induced

    D. combination forced and induced

_____ **26.** The purpose of the fuel oil return line is to ___.
      A. circulate fuel oil during warm-up
      B. return fuel oil that bypasses the burner
      C. return fuel oil from the relief valve
      D. all of the above

_____ **27.** Duplex strainers are found on ___ of the fuel oil pump.
      A. the suction side
      B. the discharge side
      C. both the suction and discharge sides
      D. none of the above

_____ **28.** Fuel oil heaters must be used when burning No. ___ fuel oil.
      A. 1
      B. 2
      C. 4
      D. 6

_____ **29.** The ___ oversees adherence to codes involving the construction and repairs of boilers and pressure vessels.
      A. EPA
      B. National Board
      C. OSHA
      D. boiler inspector

_____ **30.** The ___ valve controls the firing rate in a high pressure gas system.
      A. solenoid
      B. manual reset
      C. check
      D. butterfly

_____ **31.** The gas pressure regulator in a low pressure gas system reduces the gas pressure to approximately ___ psi.
      A. 0
      B. 5
      C. 10
      D. 15

_____ **32.** Boilers are equipped with a combination burner for ___.
      A. higher pressure operation
      B. more flexible operation
      C. safer operation
      D. higher rates of combustion

_____ **33.** Draft is measured in ___.
     A. pounds per square inch
     B. inches or tenths of an inch of a vertical water column
     C. inches or tenths of an inch of mercury
     D. ounces per square inch

_____ **34.** ___ draft uses a fan before and after the boiler.
     A. Forced
     B. Induced
     C. Natural
     D. combination forced and induced

_____ **35.** The amount of draft available in a natural draft system is dependent on the ___.
     A. water pressure
     B. height of the chimney
     C. fly ash in the gases of combustion
     D. types of fans used

_____ **36.** Mechanical draft is produced by the ___.
     A. height of the chimney
     B. diameter of the chimney
     C. power-driven fans
     D. steam jets

_____ **37.** Mechanical draft can be classified as ___.
     A. pressurized
     B. natural
     C. regenerative
     D. forced or induced

_____ **38.** The induced draft fan is located ___.
     A. between the boiler and the chimney
     B. at the base of the chimney
     C. at the burner
     D. in the first pass of the gases of combustion

_____ **39.** Mechanical draft can be used when burning ___.
     A. fuel oil
     B. coal
     C. gas
     D. all of the above

_____ **40.** The type of draft used in a fireplace is ___ draft.
     A. mechanical
     B. natural
     C. forced
     D. combination

_____ **41.** Anthracite coal has a high ___ content.
       A. lignite
       B. fixed carbon
       C. moisture
       D. volatile

_____ **42.** When the temperature of fuel oil is raised, its viscosity ___.
       A. remains the same
       B. is raised
       C. is lowered
       D. cannot be affected by heat

_____ **43.** The temperature at which fuel oil gives off a vapor that ignites readily when exposed to an open flame is its ___ point.
       A. flash
       B. fire
       C. pour
       D. viscosity

_____ **44.** The lowest temperature at which fuel oil will flow is its ___ point.
       A. flash
       B. fire
       C. pour
       D. viscosity

_____ **45.** A ___ is burner control equipment that monitors the burner start-up sequence and the main flame during normal operation.
       A. flue gas analyzer
       B. modulation control system
       C. flame safeguard system
       D. none of the above

Name _____ Date _____

True-False

T   F   **1.** Blowdown of the boiler is not required if proper feedwater treatment is used.

T   F   **2.** Try cocks on a water column can be used to determine the water level if the gauge glass is broken.

T   F   **3.** The low water fuel cutoff shuts off the fuel to the burner when a low water condition exists.

T   F   **4.** The water column reduces water turbulence to allow a more accurate reading in the gauge glass.

T   F   **5.** Blowing down the water column and gauge glass too frequently can cause a false water level.

T   F   **6.** A stop valve on the feedwater line closest to the shell of the boiler allows repair of the check valve without dumping the boiler.

T   F   **7.** The vacuum pump and condensate tank are designed to discharge air and pump water.

T   F   **8.** Makeup water is added when the boiler water is above the NOWL.

T   F   **9.** Most makeup water contains some scale-forming salts.

T   F   **10.** A globe valve should never be used as a main steam stop valve.

T   F   **11.** When open, gate valves offer no restriction to flow.

Multiple Choice

_____ **1.** The purpose of the ON/OFF pressure control is to ___.
   A. open and close the water column
   B. regulate air flow
   C. regulate fuel flow
   D. start and stop the burner on steam pressure demand

_____ **2.** A steam siphon ensures that ___ does not enter the boiler pressure control.
   A. steam
   B. water
   C. air
   D. gas

_____ **3.** The flame scanner is sensitive to ___.
   A. heat
   B. temperature
   C. pressure
   D. infrared rays

_____ **4.** In the event of a flame failure, the programmer ___.
   A. sends more fuel to start a new firing cycle
   B. secures the fuel and purges the furnace
   C. vents the firetubes
   D. stops the induced draft fan

_____ **5.** Pressure gauges are calibrated in pounds per ___.
   A. square foot
   B. cubic inch
   C. vertical inch
   D. square inch

_____ **6.** The boiler steam pressure gauge must be connected to the ___ of the boiler.
   A. lowest part of the steam side
   B. lowest part of the water side
   C. highest part of the steam side
   D. highest part of the water side

_____ **7.** Vacuum gauges are calibrated in inches of ___ atmospheric pressure.
   A. mercury below
   B. water below
   C. mercury above
   D. water above

_____ **8.** Boiler water must be treated to prevent ___.
   A. formation of scale
   B. overpressure
   C. flame failure
   D. none of the above

_____ **9.** Oxygen in the boiler causes ___.
   A. scale
   B. pitting of boiler metal
   C. caustic embrittlement
   D. carryover

_____ **10.** Carryover can lead to ___.
   A. excess fuel oil temperature
   B. water hammer
   C. gas overpressure
   D. air in the feedwater lines

_____ **11.** Oxygen present in water is commonly removed by ___.
  A. adding lead sulfide
  B. heating the feedwater
  C. using the bottom blowdown valves
  D. using the surface blowdown valves

_____ **12.** When taking over a shift, the boiler operator first checks the ___.
  A. boiler room log
  B. fuel oil supply
  C. water level on all boilers that are on the line
  D. bottom blowdown valves

_____ **13.** The purpose of a flame safeguard system is to protect the boiler from ___.
  A. improper fuel oil pressure
  B. a possible furnace explosion
  C. exceeding its MAWP
  D. starting in low fire

_____ **14.** After verifying the proper boiler water level, the burner may be started after ___.
  A. filling the vacuum tank
  B. venting the drum condenser
  C. purging the furnace
  D. purging the superheater

_____ **15.** As the boiler is cooling down, the boiler operator must maintain the ___.
  A. NOWL
  B. excess air
  C. normal feedwater temperature
  D. 10% CO_2 reading

_____ **16.** Boilers that are out of service for an extended period of time ___.
  A. are stored with an NOWL
  B. are filled with oxygen
  C. require more than 8 psi in the boiler
  D. require proper layup procedures

_____ **17.** If there is a danger of the boiler freezing, the boiler should be laid up ___.
  A. with a light fire
  B. by using steam from the header to keep the boiler warm
  C. dry with all water removed
  D. using an antifreeze

_____ **18.** A low water fuel cutoff ___.
  A. shuts the burner down
  B. increases steam pressure to the load
  C. adds water to the boiler
  D. purges the boiler furnace

_____ **19.** A boiler that has had a low water condition should be ___.
        A. thoroughly examined for signs of overheating
        B. thoroughly examined for scale buildup
        C. brought up to full steam pressure to test for leaks
        D. brought up to the MAWP as soon as possible

_____ **20.** Flame scanners are ___.
        A. equipped with a flame sensor
        B. found on fuel oil strainers
        C. found only on high pressure boilers
        D. found only on low pressure boilers

_____ **21.** A furnace explosion can be caused by ___.
        A. excess draft
        B. a low steam pressure condition
        C. an overheated furnace
        D. an accumulation of fuel vapors

_____ **22.** Class ___ fires burn oil, grease, paint, and other flammable liquids.
        A. A
        B. B
        C. C
        D. D

_____ **23.** An unsafe condition should be reported to the ___.
        A. shift operator
        B. immediate supervisor
        C. fire department
        D. plant personnel department

_____ **24.** To start and sustain a fire, ___ are required.
        A. fuel, heat, and CO_2
        B. fuel, combustible matter, and CO_2
        C. fuel, heat, and nitrogen
        D. fuel, heat, and oxygen

_____ **25.** A fire caused by the ignition of wood, paper, or textiles is a Class ___ fire.
        A. A
        B. B
        C. C
        D. D

_____ **26.** A ___ is the use of locks, chains, or other physical restraints to prevent the operation of equipment.
        A. lockout
        B. tagout
        C. permit authorization
        D. restriction form

_____ **27.** The low water fuel cutoff should be blown down ___.
  A. daily or more often
  B. monthly
  C. every six months
  D. during annual inspection

_____ **28.** The ___ senses the water temperature in a boiler.
  A. low water fuel cutoff
  B. aquastat
  C. vaporstat
  D. feedwater regulator

_____ **29.** A drop in water level in a steam boiler causes the automatic feedwater regulator to ___.
  A. close the fuel oil solenoid valve
  B. increase the flow of feedwater
  C. reduce the flow of feedwater
  D. increase the fuel oil to the burner

_____ **30.** A ___ is a regulation or minimum requirement.
  A. standard
  B. code
  C. technical bulletin
  D. recommendation

_____ **31.** In the safe operation of a steam boiler, the most important rule to follow is to ___.
  A. fill out the boiler room log
  B. perform bottom blowdowns regularly
  C. read the operation manual daily
  D. maintain the proper boiler water level at all times

_____ **32.** The purpose of try cocks is to ___.
  A. remove sludge and sediment
  B. determine the water level in the boiler
  C. draw water samples
  D. blow down the gauge

_____ **33.** A(n) ___ valve is allowed between the boiler shell and the safety valve.
  A. os&y
  B. lever
  C. check
  D. none of the above

_____ **34.** A low pressure steam boiler safety valve setting cannot exceed ___ psi.
  A. 15
  B. 20
  C. 25
  D. 160

_____ **35.** ___ allow for the movement caused by expansion and contraction of steam lines from heating and cooling.
    A. Lagging joints
    B. Convection valves
    C. Bellow plates
    D. Expansion bends

_____ **36.** In a flame safeguard firing cycle, before the fuel oil valve can open, the flame scanner must first ___.
    A. purge the furnace
    B. prove pilot ignition
    C. prove water level
    D. start feedwater flow

_____ **37.** The low water fuel cutoff should be tested ___.
    A. with the burner firing
    B. with the burner off
    C. by removing the flame scanner
    D. once a heating season

_____ **38.** If the low water alarm starts ringing, ___.
    A. secure the burner and feedwater
    B. blow down the water column
    C. add feedwater quickly and reduce the firing rate
    D. start another feedwater pump

_____ **39.** The most accurate method used to determine the amount of feedwater treatment required is ___.
    A. boiler water analysis
    B. measurement of feedwater pressure
    C. measurement of blowdown pressure
    D. checking boiler water temperature

_____ **40.** The boiler vent should be kept open when ___.
    A. the boiler is warmed up
    B. the boiler has maximum line pressure
    C. steam is blowing out of the vent
    D. the boiler is cut off the line

_____ **41.** To perform an evaporation test on the low water fuel cutoff, ___.
    A. have the chief engineer in attendance
    B. close the main steam stop valve
    C. secure all feedwater and makeup water going to the boiler
    D. completely drain the low water fuel cutoff float chamber

Name _____ Date _____

True-False

T   F   **1.** Steam boilers that are out of service for an extended period require proper lay-up.

T   F   **2.** The dry method of boiler lay-up requires the boiler to be left open with air circulated to keep the boiler drums and tubes dry.

T   F   **3.** Chemical treatment of boiler water is not required for wet layup if the water has been deaerated.

T   F   **4.** The flash point of fuel oil is lower than the fire point.

T   F   **5.** The fire point of fuel oil is the minimum temperature at which fuel oil burns continuously.

T   F   **6.** No. 6 fuel oil burns with a clean flame when it is not heated.

T   F   **7.** If the gasket leaks on a duplex strainer, air could be drawn into the fuel oil lines.

T   F   **8.** Dirty strainers produce low suction readings.

T   F   **9.** Rotary cup burners can only burn No. 2 fuel oil.

T   F   **10.** Air used to atomize fuel oil is primary air.

T   F   **11.** Combination burners are used only in high pressure plants.

Multiple Choice

_____   **1.** A ___ should be used to clean the inside of a gauge glass.
A. wire brush
B. cloth wrapped around a wooden dowel
C. screwdriver wrapped with a paper towel
D. sandpaper mounted on a steel rod

_____   **2.** A ___ is an accepted reference or practice.
A. standard
B. code
C. recommendation
D. none of the above

115

_____ **3.** An aquastat is an automatic device that senses ___.
A. water pressure
B. steam pressure
C. water temperature
D. steam temperature

_____ **4.** At pressures higher than atmospheric pressure, water boils at ___.
A. less than 212°F
B. exactly 212°F
C. more than 212°F
D. temperature cannot be determined

_____ **5.** The number of blowdowns a boiler requires is determined by ___.
A. boiler water analysis
B. checking chimney temperature
C. boiler manufacturer data
D. steam flow in the plant

_____ **6.** Complete combustion is the combustion of fuel with ___.
A. the theoretical amount of air
B. the minimum amount of excess air
C. no excess air
D. no smoke or CO_2

_____ **7.** Oxygen in the boiler causes ___.
A. priming
B. foaming
C. pitting
D. carryover

_____ **8.** No. ___ fuel oil has the highest heating value in Btu/gal.
A. 2
B. 4
C. 5
D. 6

_____ **9.** The amount of ___ draft produced is affected by the temperature outside.
A. natural
B. forced
C. induced
D. balanced

_____ **10.** To prepare a boiler for inspection, the boiler should be ___.
A. at MAWP
B. on-line
C. cool, open, and thoroughly clean
D. ready to dump when the inspector arrives

_____ **11.** Information on the boiler nameplate includes ___.
   A. MAWP
   B. date of manufacture
   C. manufacturer
   D. all of the above

_____ **12.** The safety valve is commonly tested during normal plant operation by the ___.
   A. chief engineer
   B. state inspector
   C. operator on duty
   D. plant manager

_____ **13.** In a straight-tube watertube boiler, heat and gases of combustion pass through the ___.
   A. tubes
   B. furnace
   C. fuel oil strainer
   D. all of the above

_____ **14.** A feedwater pump can become steambound if ___.
   A. steam pressure is too high
   B. water pressure is too high
   C. steam pressure is too low
   D. feedwater temperature is too high

_____ **15.** When burning No. 6 fuel oil, a(n) ___ is needed.
   A. fuel oil heater
   B. feedwater heater
   C. air preheater
   D. none of the above

_____ **16.** The height of the chimney determines the amount of ___ draft.
   A. forced
   B. induced
   C. combination forced and induced
   D. natural

_____ **17.** The water column on a low pressure boiler is used to ___.
   A. measure the water level
   B. indicated steam pressure
   C. reduce turbulence in the gauge glass
   D. water columns are never used on low pressure boilers

_____ **18.** To protect against a furnace explosion, ___.
   A. keep the water side clean
   B. purge the boiler after all flame failures
   C. check the damper
   D. test safety valves once a week

_____ **19.** A water column should be blown down ___.
    A. once a day
    B. once a month
    C. once a shift
    D. when taking a boiler off-line

_____ **20.** The amount of fire in the burner is controlled by a(n) ___.
    A. vaporstat
    B. operating pressure control
    C. aquastat
    D. modulating pressure control

_____ **21.** A clogged duplex fuel oil strainer located on the suction side of the pump results in ___.
    A. a high discharge pressure
    B. a high reading on the suction gauge
    C. a high fuel oil temperature
    D. increased fuel oil consumption

_____ **22.** A fan located between the breeching and chimney is a(n) ___ fan.
    A. chimney
    B. breeching
    C. forced draft
    D. induced draft

_____ **23.** ___ is when water is carried over from the boiler into the steam lines.
    A. Purging
    B. Chattering
    C. Throttling
    D. Priming

_____ **24.** Impurities on the surface of the water in a steam and water drum are removed by a(n) ___.
    A. continuous blowdown
    B. intermittent blowdown
    C. surface blowdown
    D. bottom blowdown

_____ **25.** A main steam stop valve is most commonly a(n) ___ valve.
    A. check
    B. globe
    C. modulating
    D. os&y gate

_____ **26.** A change in the condensate return temperature can be caused by a malfunctioning ___.
    A. feedwater pump
    B. fuel oil pump
    C. steam trap
    D. fuel oil strainer

_____ **27.** A pressure control on a steam boiler is used to ___.

    A. control operating fuel oil temperature

    B. control makeup water pressure

    C. control high and low fire

    D. start and stop the breeching cleanout

_____ **28.** Pressure at the discharge side of a forced draft fan is ___ atmospheric pressure.

    A. less than

    B. more than

    C. the same as

    D. balanced at

_____ **29.** Before dumping a boiler, ___.

    A. allow the boiler to cool

    B. call the inspector

    C. open the blowdown valve with 5 to 10 psi on the boiler

    D. open all surface blowdown valves

_____ **30.** Water weighs approximately ___ lb/gal.

    A. 1.0

    B. 8.3

    C. 62.4

    D. 212

_____ **31.** Foaming of water results when the water is contaminated with foreign material that causes ___.

    A. an increase in makeup water added

    B. more blowdowns

    C. an increase in fuel consumption

    D. an increase in surface tension

_____ **32.** Blowing down is most effective when the steam output is ___.

    A. at a high rate

    B. at a low rate

    C. at zero

    D. early in the shift

_____ **33.** The water column must be located ___.

    A. on the right side of the boiler

    B. on the left side of the boiler

    C. on the front of the boiler

    D. at the NOWL

_____ **34.** The low water fuel cutoff should be tested with an evaporation test ___.

    A. daily

    B. weekly

    C. monthly

    D. yearly

_____ **35.** A pressure control is protected from live steam by a ___.
        A. stop valve
        B. try cock
        C. siphon
        D. check valve

_____ **36.** A boiler produces black smoke when there is ___.
        A. low atmospheric pressure
        B. an improper mixture of air and fuel
        C. excess secondary air
        D. excess primary air

_____ **37.** In order to properly test the low water fuel cutoff, ___.
        A. the burner must be OFF
        B. there must be no pressure on the boiler
        C. the burner must be firing
        D. the fuel must be shut OFF

_____ **38.** The purpose of an expansion tank in a hot water heating system is to allow for the expansion of ___.
        A. water
        B. hot air
        C. air and steam
        D. gas in the burner

_____ **39.** The flame scanner is located on the ___.
        A. main steam line
        B. fuel oil line
        C. front of the furnace
        D. bottom blowdown line

_____ **40.** The pressure control controls the boiler operating range by ___.
        A. regulating the fuel oil pressure
        B. starting and stopping the burner
        C. changes in water temperature
        D. causing the safety valve to relieve pressure

_____ **41.** A heavy accumulation of soot on a boiler heating surface results in ___.
        A. loss of boiler efficiency
        B. increased heat transfer
        C. loss of fire
        D. safety valve popping

Name _____ **Date** _____

True-False

T   F   **1.** A low water condition is a common cause of boiler room accidents.

T   F   **2.** A steam pressure gauge is calibrated in pounds per square foot.

T   F   **3.** The Bourdon tube of a steam pressure gauge must be protected from live steam.

T   F   **4.** A bottom blowdown line returns water to the boiler.

T   F   **5.** The functions of a steam trap are to remove air and condensate without the loss of steam.

T   F   **6.** Purging a furnace before firing can prevent a furnace explosion.

T   F   **7.** Boilers burning soft coal require large furnace volume to complete combustion.

T   F   **8.** Smoke is a sign of incomplete combustion.

T   F   **9.** The furnace must be purged after any flame failure.

T   F   **10.** An induced draft fan is located on the front of the boiler.

T   F   **11.** When using natural draft, there is a limit to the amount of fuel that can be burned.

T   F   **12.** A forced draft fan is located in the breeching.

T   F   **13.** Oxygen in the boiler water is used to remove nonadhering sludge.

Multiple Choice

_____   **1.** An ignition failure can be detected by the ___.
　　　　　　　　　　　A. low water fuel cutoff
　　　　　　　　　　　B. feedwater makeup system
　　　　　　　　　　　C. high fire control
　　　　　　　　　　　D. flame scanner

_____   **2.** An automatic feedwater regulator is used to ___.
　　　　　　　　　　　A. ensure the proper water level in the boiler
　　　　　　　　　　　B. shut off the burner in the event of low water
　　　　　　　　　　　C. control the burner operating range
　　　　　　　　　　　D. modulate gas pressure to the burner

_____ 3. On a steam boiler, testing the operation of the safety valve by hand with the boiler under pressure should be performed ___.
    A. at the start of each heating season
    B. every 30 days
    C. annually
    D. when maximum water pressure is achieved

_____ 4. In a natural circulation hot water heating system, excess water is collected in the ___.
    A. aquastat
    B. blowdown tank
    C. expansion tank
    D. relief valve tank

_____ 5. If ignition fails during burner startup, the ___ protects the boiler.
    A. low water fuel cutoff
    B. flame scanner
    C. vaporstat
    D. aquastat

_____ 6. The ___ is the automatic control that protects a boiler from being fired with a low water condition.
    A. aquastat
    B. whistle valve
    C. low water fuel cutoff
    D. flame scanner

_____ 7. An indication of incomplete combustion is ___.
    A. increased combustion efficiency
    B. black smoke from the chimney
    C. an increase in water level
    D. higher steam pressure generated

_____ 8. A(n) ___ pressure control controls the amount of steam produced by varying the firing rate.
    A. safety
    B. ON/OFF
    C. modulating
    D. aquastat

_____ 9. The ___ operates by sensing boiler water temperature.
    A. flame scanner
    B. vaporstat
    C. aquastat
    D. pressure control

_____ 10. The purpose of performing a try lever test on a safety valve is to ___.
    A. test valve operation
    B. set the operating range of the boiler
    C. test popping pressure
    D. determine the NOWL

_____ **11.** A feedwater regulator depends on the operation of a ___.
     A. water pressure solenoid
     B. steam pressure orifice
     C. water temperature gauge
     D. float-controlled valve

_____ **12.** Furnace explosions can be prevented by ___.
     A. blowing down the low water fuel cutoff daily
     B. testing the safety valve daily
     C. purging the furnace after any flame failure
     D. none of the above

_____ **13.** To increase ___, the height of the chimney must be increased.
     A. forced draft
     B. induced draft
     C. natural draft
     D. combustion gas

_____ **14.** In most plants, the water column and gauge glass should be blown down at least ___.
     A. each 8-hour shift
     B. monthly
     C. quarterly
     D. annually

_____ **15.** When blowing down the low water fuel cutoff, ___.
     A. more fuel is burned
     B. the burner shuts off
     C. steam pressure increases
     D. condensate temperature increases

_____ **16.** The purpose of the aquastat is to ___.
     A. control the operating temperature range of a hot water heating boiler
     B. feed water to the system
     C. maintain a minimum water level in the boiler
     D. provide for the expansion of water

_____ **17.** A pressure-reducing valve in a hot water heating system ___.
     A. maintains a specified water pressure in the boiler
     B. shuts the burner OFF when there is low water in the boiler
     C. reduces makeup water pressure
     D. regulates the flow of steam from the boiler

_____ **18.** A relief valve is rated in ___ per hour.
     A. NOWL
     B. Btu
     C. psi
     D. gallons

_____ **19.** Makeup water fed to the boiler is ___.
        A. treated feedwater fed to the burner
        B. water added to the boiler
        C. condensate return water
        D. none of the above

_____ **20.** The water column outlets of a steam boiler are connected to the ___.
        A. mud drum
        B. blowdown line
        C. water and steam section of a steam boiler
        D. water tubes of the boiler

_____ **21.** A low pressure boiler commonly receives makeup water from the ___.
        A. boiler feed pump
        B. injector
        C. automatic city water makeup feeder
        D. return lines

_____ **22.** A pressure control is protected from live steam by a(n) ___.
        A. mercury switch
        B. shutoff valve
        C. siphon
        D. inspector's test valve

_____ **23.** The safety valve is located ___.
        A. in the blowdown line
        B. on the main steam header
        C. on the highest part of the steam side of the boiler
        D. on the try cock

_____ **24.** In most states, the only type of safety valve allowed on steam boilers is the ___ type.
        A. lever
        B. direct-loaded pop
        C. spring-loaded pop-off
        D. vacuum relief

_____ **25.** A stop valve and a check valve are usually placed ___.
        A. in the steam line leaving a watertube boiler
        B. in the blowdown line of a firetube boiler
        C. as close to the boiler as possible on the feedwater line
        D. in line with the pressure control

_____ **26.** The steam gauge is calibrated in ___.
        A. pounds of pressure
        B. inches of pressure
        C. pounds per square inch
        D. pounds per square foot

_____ **27.** No. 6 fuel oil ___.
    A. is atomized as it leaves the fuel oil tank
    B. is mixed with No. 2 fuel oil before it is atomized
    C. must be heated before it can be burned
    D. has a lower heating value than No. 2 fuel oil

_____ **28.** A compound pressure gauge indicates ___.
    A. the difference in pressure
    B. the sum of two line pressures
    C. either pressure or vacuum
    D. three different pressures at the same time

_____ **29.** At NOWL using try cocks, ___.
    A. water only is discharged out of the top try cock
    B. steam only is discharged out of the bottom try cock
    C. steam and water are discharged out of the bottom try cock
    D. steam and water are discharged out of the middle try cock

_____ **30.** The purpose of the feedwater regulator is to ___.
    A. sound an alarm if the water level in the boiler is too high
    B. maintain the proper water level in the boiler
    C. shut off the burner if the water gets too low
    D. keep the steam pressure within the safe limits

_____ **31.** The low water fuel cutoff should be blown down ___.
    A. every day
    B. once a month
    C. at the end of the heating season
    D. once a week

_____ **32.** When a low water condition occurs, the low water fuel cutoff ___.
    A. increases the feedwater supply to the boiler
    B. sounds an alarm to warn of low water
    C. shuts off the fuel supply and feedwater to the burner
    D. places the boiler in low fire

_____ **33.** To obtain an accurate reading of the water level in the gauge glass, ___.
    A. add city water makeup
    B. use the bottom blowdown valve
    C. blow down the gauge glass
    D. open all try cocks

_____ **34.** To change the operating pressure of a steam boiler, ___.
    A. adjust the fuel supply
    B. use the bottom blowdown valve wide and then close it
    C. adjust the pressure control
    D. look at the gauge glass

_____ **35.** A lead sulfide cell is used in a(n) ___.
    A. pressure control
    B. flame scanner
    C. low water fuel cutoff
    D. evaporation test

_____ **36.** When performing a hydrostatic test on a boiler, the safety valves must be ___.
    A. kept free to pop at a set pressure
    B. opened
    C. plugged at the discharge end
    D. gagged or removed and the opening must be blank flanged

_____ **37.** A feedwater pump is used to ___.
    A. pump water into a boiler
    B. pump out the boiler room sump pit
    C. circulate water through the hot water heating system
    D. pump fuel oil to the fuel oil burner

_____ **38.** The blowdown line can discharge to a ___.
    A. blowdown separator
    B. heat exchanger
    C. blowdown tank
    D. all of the above

_____ **39.** The heating surface of a boiler is ___.
    A. only in the furnace
    B. only found on water tube boilers
    C. that part of the boiler where water is located
    D. the part of the boiler where water is on one side and gases of combustion are on the other side

_____ **40.** The range of the steam pressure gauge is ___.
    A. 1½ to 2 times the MAWP
    B. the MAWP
    C. not more than 6% over the MAWP
    D. gauge plus atmospheric pressure

_____ **41.** For every foot of vertical piping filled with water, there is hydrostatic pressure of ___ psi.
    A. 0.433
    B. 0.251
    C. 0.144
    D. 0.0433

Name _____ Date _____

True-False

T   F   **1.** In a low pressure gas burner, the gas regulator reduces gas pressure to 0 psi.

T   F   **2.** A refrigerant absorbs heat in the evaporator of a compression refrigeration system.

T   F   **3.** The range of a steam pressure gauge should be at least 3 times the MAWP of the boiler.

T   F   **4.** The temperature and pressure of a refrigerant in a compression refrigeration system is lowered when it is compressed.

T   F   **5.** An absorption refrigeration system can use ammonia as the refrigerant.

T   F   **6.** Sensible heat is the amount of heat that changes the measurable temperature of a substance but not its state.

T   F   **7.** The mechanical energy of a compressor can be changed to heat energy in a refrigeration system.

T   F   **8.** An aquastat is used on a compression tank to control flow to the circulating pump.

T   F   **9.** A Scotch marine boiler is a type of firetube boiler.

T   F   **10.** A pressure control regulates the firing of the burner based on condensate return flow.

T   F   **11.** A feedwater check valve is commonly installed between the stop valve and the boiler.

T   F   **12.** In colder climates, No. 6 fuel oil requires the use of tank heaters.

T   F   **13.** Cooling systems are commonly rated in Btu of cooling per hour.

T   F   **14.** Perfect combustion occurs when a boiler has no soot in the gases of combustion.

T   F   **15.** Scale is caused by an accumulation of minerals present in boiler water.

Multiple Choice

_____ **1.** Combustion efficiency in the burner is controlled by ___.
  A. primary air
  B. secondary air
  C. forced combustion gas
  D. all of the above

127

_____ **2.** In a compression system, liquid refrigerant under high pressure is allowed to drop in pressure by the ___.
A. absorber
B. absorbent
C. metering device
D. condenser

_____ **3.** The capacity of a safety valve is measured by the amount of steam that can be discharged per ___.
A. shift
B. minute
C. hour
D. blowdown

_____ **4.** Heat added to a substance that changes its state without a change in temperature is ___ heat.
A. super
B. sensible
C. latent
D. mechanical

_____ **5.** In a refrigeration system, heat is ___ when a fluid changes from a gas to a liquid.
A. decreased
B. absorbed
C. released
D. compressed

_____ **6.** A(n) ___ is printed material used to relay chemical hazard information from the manufacturer to the employee.
A. OSHA regulation
B. MSDS
C. EPA specification sheet
D. ASME notice

_____ **7.** Excessive water in the boiler can lead to ___.
A. scale deposits
B. water hammer
C. flame failure
D. all of the above

_____ **8.** The ___ is a government regulatory agency that was established to control and abate pollution.
A. DOT
B. OSHA
C. ANSI
D. EPA

_____ **9.** An absorption cooling system does not include a(n) ___.
A. condenser
B. compressor
C. evaporator
D. generator

_____ **10.** In a lithium bromide and water cooling system, refrigerant is heated with a steam coil in the ___.
    A. evaporator
    B. compressor
    C. generator
    D. condenser

_____ **11.** A Bourdon tube is used in a(n) ___.
    A. compression tank
    B. evaporator
    C. compressor
    D. none of the above

_____ **12.** Air used in the combustion process is classified as ___ air.
    A. primary
    B. secondary
    C. excess
    D. all of the above

_____ **13.** In the low pressure zone of a compression refrigeration system, ___ by the refrigerant.
    A. heat is absorbed
    B. steam pressure is increased
    C. lithium bromide is produced
    D. ammonia vapors are generated

_____ **14.** Soot buildup on heating surfaces acts as an ___ to prevent the transfer of heat.
    A. evaporator
    B. insulator
    C. ionizer
    D. all of the above

_____ **15.** Absorption cooling systems commonly use ___ as a refrigerant.
    A. R-134a only
    B. R-134a and water
    C. ammonia only
    D. ammonia and water

_____ **16.** Flame scanners can use a ___ to sense infrared rays of the pilot light and main burner.
    A. lead sulfide cell
    B. solenoid
    C. purge sensor
    D. all of the above

_____ **17.** In a compression refrigeration system, high pressure vapor is converted from a gas to a liquid in the ___.
    A. evaporator
    B. compressor
    C. generator
    D. condenser

_____ **18.** Oxygen is removed from the boiler water by ___ the water.
     A. adding minerals to
     B. chilling
     C. heating
     D. all of the above

_____ **19.** In a compression refrigeration system, the refrigerant absorbs heat in the ___.
     A. diverter valve
     B. compressor
     C. generator
     D. none of the above

_____ **20.** Steam that has released its heat turns to ___.
     A. evaporated steam
     B. sensible steam
     C. condensate
     D. latent vapors

_____ **21.** A low water fuel cutoff should be tested ___.
     A. daily
     B. monthly
     C. quarterly
     D. annually

_____ **22.** Some ___ containing chlorofluorocarbons (CFCs) cause damage to the earth's ozone layer.
     A. lithium bromides
     B. nitrogen fuels
     C. steam generators
     D. refrigerants

_____ **23.** The burning of all of the fuel in the burner using the minimum amount of air is ___ combustion.
     A. perfect
     B. theoretical
     C. complete
     D. incomplete

_____ **24.** The temperature at which fuel oil must be heated to burn continuously when exposed to an open flame is the ___ point.
     A. fire
     B. flash
     C. ignition
     D. thermal

_____ **25.** Water used as a medium in indirect cooling systems must be kept above ___°F.
     A. 0
     B. 22
     C. 32
     D. 212

_____ **26.** Combustibles in a Class A fire are ___.
        A. grease and gasoline
        B. paper and wood
        C. paints and solvents
        D. electrical equipment

_____ **27.** The furnace must be ___ after every flame failure.
        A. cleaned
        B. blown down
        C. purged
        D. pressurized

_____ **28.** The heating value of a fuel oil is expressed in ___.
        A. tons of heating
        B. therms
        C. flame units
        D. British thermal units

_____ **29.** Hard or ___ coal produces less smoke than soft coal.
        A. anthracite
        B. bituminous
        C. volatile
        D. none of the above

_____ **30.** A low pressure steam boiler has a MAWP of ___ psi.
        A. 5
        B. 10
        C. 25
        D. none of the above

_____ **31.** There are no tubes in a ___ boiler.
        A. cast iron sectional
        B. vertical wet-top
        C. Scotch marine
        D. multiple-pass dry top

_____ **32.** Pressure in the high pressure side of a compression refrigeration system is produced by the ___.
        A. expansion valve
        B. condenser
        C. compressor
        D. evaporator

_____ **33.** In a refrigeration system, heat is ___ when a fluid changes from a liquid to a gas.
        A. produced
        B. absorbed
        C. released
        D. all of the above

_____ **34.** The most common medium used to transport heat from an area to be cooled is ___.
  A. water
  B. ammonia
  C. freon and water
  D. all of the above

_____ **35.** Boiler fittings are manufactured in accordance with the ___ code.
  A. boiler certification
  B. ASME
  C. NFPA
  D. OSHA

_____ **36.** Boiler water level can be determined using the ___ if the gauge glass is broken.
  A. pressure gauge
  B. siphon gauge
  C. try cocks
  D. leveling stick

_____ **37.** A ___ blowdown is performed to reduce foaming of the boiler water.
  A. bottom
  B. surface
  C. priming
  D. huddling

_____ **38.** Hot water boilers operating with a 250°F water temperature and ___ psi water pressure or less are classified as low pressure.
  A. 15
  B. 100
  C. 160
  D. 212

_____ **39.** Oxygen in boiler water causes ___.
  A. corrosion
  B. rusting
  C. pitting
  D. all of the above

_____ **40.** A(n) ___ control system controls the amount of steam produced by changing the burner firing rate.
  A. modulating
  B. ON/OFF
  C. proving
  D. indirect

_____ **41.** Safety valves are repaired by ___.
  A. the operator as required
  B. an authorized manufacturer representative
  C. the boiler inspector
  D. the plant manager

Name _____ **Date** _____

Essay

1. What is the first thing a boiler operator must do when taking over a shift?

2. What steps must be taken if steam comes out of the bottom try cock?

3. When steps must be taken if water comes out of the top try cock?

4. What are the different ways of getting water into the boiler?

5. What is the function of a pressure control?

6. How are safety valves tested?

7. How often should safety valves be tested?

8. What is the function of a low water fuel cutoff?

9. How is a low water fuel cutoff tested?

10. How often should a safety valve pop on a low pressure steam boiler?

11. At what pressure should a safety valve pop on a low pressure steam boiler?

12. What is meant by purging the furnace?

13. What is the most important valve on the boiler?

14. How often should a boiler have a bottom blowdown?

15. How is the flame scanner tested?

16. What methods can be used to determine the water level in the boiler?

17. What is the main cause of smoke?

18. What are the different types of draft used in boilers?

19. What is the function of a check valve on the feedwater line?

20. What is the function of a stop valve on the feedwater line?

21. What actions would be required if the safety valve was popping and the steam pressure indicated 30 psi on the boiler?

22. What is meant by perfect, complete, and incomplete combustion?

133

23. What could cause a furnace explosion?

24. What are the steps necessary for preparing for a boiler inspection?

25. How often should a gauge glass be blown down?

26. What is the difference between a forced circulation hot water heating system and a natural circulation hot water heating system?

27. What procedure is followed when performing a hydrostatic test on a boiler?

28. What does the abbreviation NOWL stand for?

29. What does the abbreviation MAWP stand for?

30. What is the cause of carryover?

31. What is the difference between natural and mechanical draft?

32. What causes a feedwater pump to become steambound?

33. What is the difference between a fast gauge and a slow gauge?

34. What is the cause of foaming in the boiler?

35. What is the difference between a gate valve and a globe valve?

36. What is the difference between a watertube and firetube boiler?

37. Where should a water column be located?

38. When is the best time to give a boiler a bottom blowdown?

39. What is the function of a boiler vent?

40. What is used to control high fire or low fire in a boiler?

41. How can a boiler operator tell when an os&y valve is in the open position?

42. What is the function of the vacuum pump?

43. How often should the automatic city water makeup feeder be blown down?

44. What are the most commonly used types of steam traps?

45. What are two methods of testing for the proper function of a steam trap?

46. How often should the fuel oil strainer be cleaned?

47. What are two commonly used types of fuel oil burners?

48. What are the advantages of using a combination burner?

49. What is meant by primary, secondary, and excess air?

50. What is the function of a flame safeguard system?

51. What is hydrostatic pressure?

52. What are three types of heat transfer that occur in a boiler?

53. What is the function of a backflow preventer?

54. Why are expansion bends sometimes required on steam lines?

55. What is an evaporation test?

56. What are the benefits of a boiler room log?

57. What is the function of an aquastat?

58. What is a compression refrigeration system?

59. What special safety precautions must be followed when entering a confined space?

60. How is a boiler operator license obtained?

61. What is the proper procedure to use when trying to stop a leak from a gauge glass washer?

62. Describe how and when the main steam stop valve should be opened when routinely starting a boiler and bringing it on-line with another boiler.

63. What is the proper procedure to follow if the boiler shuts down, there is no water in the gauge glass, and the feedwater pump is running dry?

64. Describe where the water level should be when preparing to start a boiler that has been off-line for several days. Why should the water level be at that level? Describe what must be done about the water level.

Additional Activities

1. Take the Sample Licensing Exams on the *Low Pressure Boilers* Interactive CD-ROM.

2. Review all Media Clips on the *Low Pressure Boilers* Interactive CD-ROM.

3. Review all Flash Cards on the *Low Pressure Boilers* Interactive CD-ROM.

4. Take the Sample Licensing Exams in Chapter 12 of *Low Pressure Boilers*.

5. Optionally, review the Master Math® Applications, Unit 1 to Unit 7, located on the *Low Pressure Boilers* Interactive CD-ROM. A link to a PDF document, Boiler Math Formulas, is provided on the Master Math® Applications home page.

STEAM LOSS THROUGH AN ORIFICE*									
Orifice Size[†]	Orifice Size[†]	Differential Pressure Across Orifice, PSIG							
		15	30	60	100	150	250	400	600
#60[‡]	0.04	1	2	4	6	10	16	26	39
³⁄₆₄″	0.0469	1	3	5	9	13	22	36	53
¹⁄₁₆″	0.0625	2	5	9	16	24	39	63	95
⁵⁄₆₄″	0.0781	4	7	15	25	37	62	99	148
³⁄₃₂″	0.0938	5	11	21	36	53	89	142	213
#38[‡]	0.1015	6	12	25	42	62	104	166	250
⁷⁄₆₄″	0.1094	7	15	29	48	73	121	193	290
⅛″	0.125	9	19	38	63	95	158	252	379
⁹⁄₆₄″	0.1406	12	24	48	80	120	200	319	479
⁵⁄₃₂″	0.1562	15	30	59	99	148	246	394	591
³⁄₁₆″	0.1875	21	43	85	142	213	355	568	852
⁷⁄₃₂″	0.2188	29	58	116	193	290	483	773	1160
¼″	0.25	38	76	151	252	379	631	1010	1515
⁹⁄₃₂″	0.2812	48	96	192	319	479	798	1278	1916
⁵⁄₁₆″	0.3125	59	118	237	394	592	986	1578	2367
¹¹⁄₃₂″	0.3438	72	143	286	477	716	1194	1910	2865
⅜″	0.375	85	170	341	568	852	1420	2272	3408
⁷⁄₁₆″	0.4375	116	232	464	773	1160	1933	3093	4639
½″	0.5	151	303	606	1010	1515	2525	4039	6059
⁹⁄₁₆″	0.5625	192	383	767	1278	1917	3195	5112	7668
⅝″	0.625	237	473	947	1578	2367	3945	6311	9467
¹¹⁄₁₆″	0.6875	286	573	1145	1909	2864	4773	7637	11,455
¾″	0.75	341	682	1363	2272	3408	5680	9088	13,632
⅞″	0.875	464	928	1856	3098	4639	7731	12,370	18,555
1-¹⁄₁₆″	1.0625	684	1368	2736	4560	6840	11,400	18,240	27,359
1-⅛″	1.25	947	1893	3787	6311	9467	15,778	25,245	37,868
1-⅝″	1.625	1600	3200	6400	10,666	15,999	26,665	42,664	63,996

* in lb/hr
† in in.
‡ drill size

137

PROPERTIES OF SATURATED STEAM

Gauge Pressure*	Absolute Pressure‡	Temperature§	Heat Content**			Specific Volume Steam V_g††
			Sensible h_f	Latent h_{fg}	Total h_g	
27.96	1	101.7	69.5	1032.9	1102.4	333.0
25.91	2	126.1	93.9	1019.7	1113.6	173.5
23.87	3	141.5	109.3	1011.3	1120.6	118.6
21.83	4	153.0	120.8	1004.9	1125.7	90.52
19.79	5	162.3	130.1	999.7	1129.8	73.42
17.75	6	170.1	137.8	995.4	1133.2	61.89
15.70	7	176.9	144.6	991.5	1136.1	53.57
13.66	8	182.9	150.7	987.9	1138.6	47.26
11.62	9	188.3	156.2	984.7	1140.9	42.32
9.58	10	193.2	161.1	981.9	1143.0	38.37
7.54	11	197.8	165.7	979.2	1144.9	35.09
5.49	12	202.0	169.9	976.7	1146.6	32.35
3.45	13	205.9	173.9	974.3	1148.2	30.01
1.41	14	209.6	177.6	972.2	1149.8	28.00
Gauge Pressure†						
0	14.7	212.0	180.2	970.6	1150.8	26.80
1	15.7	215.4	183.6	968.4	1152.0	25.20
2	16.7	218.5	186.8	966.4	1153.2	23.80
3	17.7	221.5	189.8	964.5	1154.3	22.50
4	18.7	224.5	192.7	962.6	1155.3	21.40
5	19.7	227.4	195.5	960.8	1156.3	20.40
6	20.7	230.0	198.1	959.2	1157.3	19.40
7	21.7	232.4	200.6	957.6	1158.2	18.60
8	22.7	234.8	203.1	956.0	1159.1	17.90
9	23.7	237.1	205.5	954.5	1160.0	17.20
10	24.7	239.4	207.9	952.9	1160.8	16.50
11	25.7	241.6	210.1	951.5	1161.6	15.90
12	26.7	243.7	212.3	950.1	1162.3	15.30
13	27.7	245.8	214.4	948.6	1163.0	14.80
14	28.7	247.9	216.4	947.3	1163.7	14.30
15	29.7	249.8	218.4	946.0	1164.4	13.90
16	30.7	251.7	220.3	944.8	1165.1	13.40
17	31.7	253.6	222.2	943.5	1165.7	13.00
18	32.7	255.4	224.0	942.4	1166.4	12.70
19	33.7	257.2	225.8	941.2	1167.0	12.30
20	34.7	258.8	227.5	940.1	1167.6	12.00
22	36.7	262.3	230.9	937.8	1168.7	11.40
24	38.7	265.3	234.2	935.8	1170.0	10.80
26	40.7	268.3	237.3	933.5	1170.8	10.30
28	42.7	271.4	240.2	931.6	1171.8	9.87
30	44.7	274.0	243.0	929.7	1172.7	9.46
32	46.7	276.7	245.9	927.6	1173.5	9.08
34	48.7	279.4	248.5	925.8	1174.3	8.73
36	50.7	281.9	251.1	924.0	1175.1	8.40
38	52.7	284.4	253.7	922.1	1175.8	8.11
40	54.7	286.7	256.1	920.4	1176.5	7.83
42	56.7	289.0	258.5	918.6	1177.1	7.57
44	58.7	291.3	260.8	917.0	1177.8	7.33
46	60.7	293.5	263.0	915.4	1178.4	7.10
48	62.7	295.6	265.2	913.8	1179.0	6.89
50	64.7	297.7	267.4	912.2	1179.6	6.68

* in Hg vac
† in psig
‡ in psia
§ in °F
** in Btu/lb
†† in cu ft/lb

COMMON ASME INTERNATIONAL BOILER CLASSIFICATIONS

Name	Description
Automatic boiler	Equipped with certain controls and limit devices per ASME code
Boiler	Closed vessel used for heating water or liquid, or for generating steam or vapor by direct application of heat
Boiler plant	One or more boilers, connecting piping, and vessels within the same premises
Hot water supply boiler	Low pressure hot water heating boiler having a volume exceeding 120 gal. or heat input exceeding 200,000 Btu/hr, or an operating temperature exceeding 200°F that provides hot water to be used externally to itself
Low pressure hot water heating boiler	Boiler in which water is heated for the purpose of supplying heat at pressures not exceeding 160 psi or temperatures not exceeding 250°F
Low pressure steam heating boiler	Boiler operated at pressures not exceeding 15 psi for steam
Power hot water boiler	Boiler used for heating water or liquid to pressure exceeding 160 psi or a temperature exceeding 250°F
Power steam boiler	Boiler in which steam or vapor is generated at pressures exceeding 15 psi
Small power boiler	Boiler with pressures exceeding 15 psi but not exceeding 100 psi and having less than 440,000 Btu/hr input

HEATING VALUES AND CHEMICAL COMPOSITION OF STANDARD GRADES OF COAL

Rank	Heating Value*	Chemical Composition†					
		Oxygen	Hydrogen	Carbon	Nitrogen	Sulfur	Ash
Anthracite	12,910	5.0	2.9	80.0	0.9	0.7	10.5
Semi-anthracite	13,770	5.0	3.9	80.4	1.1	1.1	8.5
Low-volatile Bituminous	14,340	5.0	4.7	81.7	1.4	1.2	6.0
Medium-volatile Bituminous	13,840	5.0	5.0	79.0	1.4	1.5	8.1
High-volatile Bituminous A	13,090	9.2	5.3	73.2	1.5	2.0	8.8
High-volatile Bituminous B	12,130	13.8	5.5	68.0	1.4	2.1	9.2
High-volatile Bituminous C	10,750	21.0	5.8	60.6	1.1	2.1	9.4
Subbituminous B	9150	29.5	6.2	52.5	1.0	1.0	9.8
Subbituminous C	8940	35.8	6.5	46.7	0.8	0.6	9.6
Lignite	6900	44.0	6.9	40.1	0.7	1.0	7.3

* in Btu/lb
† in %

PIPE FITTINGS AND VALVES

	FLANGED	SCREWED	BELL & SPIGOT		FLANGED	SCREWED	BELL & SPIGOT		FLANGED	SCREWED	BELL & SPIGOT
BUSHING				REDUCING FLANGE				AUTOMATIC BY-PASS VALVE			
CAP				BULL PLUG				AUTOMATIC REDUCING VALVE			
REDUCING CROSS				PIPE PLUG				STRAIGHT CHECK VALVE			
STRAIGHT-SIZE CROSS				CONCENTRIC REDUCER				COCK			
CROSSOVER				ECCENTRIC REDUCER							
45 ELBOW				SLEEVE				DIAPHRAGM VALVE			
90 ELBOW				STRAIGHT-SIZE TEE				FLOAT VALVE			
ELBOW — TURNED DOWN				TEE – OUTLET UP				GATE VALVE			
ELBOW — TURNED UP				TEE – OUTLET DOWN				MOTOR-OPERATED GATE VALVE			
BASE ELBOW				DOUBLE-SWEEP TEE				GLOBE VALVE			
DOUBLE-BRANCH ELBOW				REDUCING TEE				MOTOR-OPERATED GLOBE VALVE			
LONG-RADIUS ELBOW				SINGLE-SWEEP TEE				ANGLE HOSE VALVE			
REDUCING ELBOW				SIDE OUTLET TEE — OUTLET DOWN							
SIDE OUTLET ELBOW — OUTLET DOWN				SIDE OUTLET TEE — OUTLET UP				GATE HOSE VALVE			
SIDE OUTLET ELBOW — OUTLET UP				UNION				GLOBE HOSE VALVE			
STREET ELBOW				ANGLE CHECK VALVE				LOCKSHIELD VALVE			
CONNECTING PIPE JOINT				ANGLE GATE VALVE — ELEVATION				QUICK-OPENING VALVE			
EXPANSION JOINT				ANGLE GATE VALVE PLAN				SAFETY VALVE			
LATERAL				ANGLE GLOBE VALVE — ELEVATION				GOVERNOR-OPERATED AUTOMATIC VALVE			
ORIFICE FLANGE				ANGLE GLOBE VALVE — PLAN							